SCHOLASTIC

NO FUSS

YEAR 2

PHOTOCOPIABLES

All you need to teach 11 curriculum subjects!

AGES

6-7

- Levelled and linked to the curriculum

- Stand-alone photocopiable activities

- Ideal for mixed-age classes

Paul Noble and Jean Noble

AUTHORS
Paul Noble and Jean Noble

DEVELOPMENT EDITOR
Kate Pedlar

PROJECT EDITOR
Fabia Lewis

DESIGNERS
Q2a Media

COVER DESIGN
Anna Oliwa

ILLUSTRATORS
Pete Smith, Ray and Corrine Burrows, Neil Gower

Text © 2008, Paul Noble and Jean Noble
© 2008, Scholastic Ltd

Published by Scholastic Ltd
Book End
Range Road
Witney
Oxfordshire
OX29 0YD
www.scholastic.co.uk

Designed using Adobe InDesign
Printed by Bell & Bain Ltd, Glasgow

2 3 4 5 6 7 8 9   0 1 2 3 4 5 6 7

British Library Cataloguing-in-Publication Data
A catalogue record for this book is available from the
British Library.

ISBN 978-1407-10094-4

Mixed Sources
Product group from well-managed
forests and other controlled sources
www.fsc.org Cert no. TT-COC-002769
© 1996 Forest Stewardship Council

www.scholastic.co.uk

CONTENTS

Introduction	5
Curriculum grid	6

CHAPTER 1
ENGLISH

Hook a word	15
Word shop	16
Long and short	17
Top-up with oil	18
Ship ahoy!	19
Ow!	20
Make and say	21
Odd word out	22
A necklace of rhymes	23
I went to town…	24
Joined-up thinking	25
Story starts	26
Dreamtime	27
What happened yesterday?	28
Mix and make families of words	29
Shopping lists	30
Asking questions: What? Where? When? Who?	31
Sorting syllables (1)	32
Sorting syllables (2)	33
At the party	34
Making sense	35
Yesterday, in the pond	36
Mandy's muddled messages	37
Wh – ch – ph	38

CHAPTER 2
MATHS

Keeping track	39
Counting on or back	40
Number vests	41
Jumping in tens	42
Odd and even numbers	43
Number patterns	44
Count and rule	45
Multiples in the air	46
Words and numbers	47
Tens and units	48
Make a date	49
More or less	50
Ten more or ten less	51
Estimate and count	52
Rounding to ten	53
Halves and quarters (1)	54
Halves and quarters (2)	55
Fractions	56
Halfway	57
Three hops	58
Less than	59
Lots of blanks	60
Sharing equally	61
Halves and doubles	62
The right sign	63
Magic squares	64
Problems	65
Measures	66
Centimetre lines	67
Lines of symmetry	68

CHAPTER 3
SCIENCE

Food on the plate (1)	69
Food on the plate (2)	70
Young and old	71
Babies and toddlers	72
Is it good for you?	73
Exploring outdoors	74
A for animal, P for plant	75
The same but different	76
How we are different	77
Natural materials	78

CONTENTS

Heat often changes things — 79
Forces — 80
Batteries — 81
Bulbs and circuits — 82
Two bulbs — 83

CHAPTER 4
HISTORY
Who was Florence Nightingale? — 84
This is Florence Nightingale — 85
Scutari hospital — 86
The Great Fire: where and when? — 87
The story of the Great Fire — 88
An eyewitness — 89

CHAPTER 5
GEOGRAPHY
Who's been on holiday? — 90
Country, town and seaside — 91
The beach — 92
The seaside 150 years ago — 93
Travel brochure — 94

CHAPTER 6
DESIGN AND TECHNOLOGY
Tractor — 95
Vehicles with a purpose — 96
Hands up! — 97
Wind-up action — 98
Hickory Dickory Dock — 99
A fishy business — 100

CHAPTER 7
ICT
Bold key presses — 101
Creating captions — 102
A burst of colour — 103
Turtle turns to treasure — 104

CHAPTER 8
ART AND DESIGN
Which way round? — 105
Design a pot — 106
Window shapes — 107
Patterns in doors — 108

CHAPTER 9
MUSIC
Feeling the pulse — 109
Copy claps — 110
A dotty game — 111
Making instruments make sound — 112
Sound resources (1) Pitch and dynamics — 113
Sound resources (2) Duration and tempo — 114
Sound story — 115

CHAPTER 10
RELIGIOUS EDUCATION
The Torah: A holy book — 116
Rules for living — 117
A story told by Jesus: The prodigal son — 118
A story told by Jesus: Firm foundations — 119
Religious celebrations — 120
Visiting places of worship — 121

CHAPTER 11
PSHE AND CITIZENSHIP
Meet the needs — 122
Needs and wants — 123
Saying no — 124
Red means danger — 125
People who help us (1) — 126
People who help us (2) — 127

www.scholastic.co.uk

INTRODUCTION

This is a straightforward compilation of stand-alone photocopiable activities for children in Year 2.

Ranging across the curriculum as they do, the activities within this book provide material for the National Curriculum subjects (except PE) plus Religious Education, PSHE and Citizenship. Although understandably not comprehensive in its National Curriculum coverage, this volume brings together a selection of previously published Scholastic photocopiables that have all been successfully tried and tested. You can use them with confidence and No Fuss.

At the heart of the book are the activity sheets presented with a concise and factual **curriculum grid**, which, in note form, cross-references the content of the sheets to: the National Curriculum, the Primary Framework, QCA schemes of work and where appropriate, to the Curriculum for Excellence (Scotland). Objectives for each activity sheet are stated and brief guidance notes are given to its use.

Within the curriculum grid, links are made to National Curriculum Attainment Targets and attainment levels as well as to the non-statutory Attainment Targets for RE.

Before you use any worksheet it is recommended that you refer to the curriculum grid so that you are clear about the objectives and are aware of any special demands made by the activity.

Teaching children of this age group can be a particular joy, certainly in our experience. Children have acquired a degree of confidence and independence that encourages the giving of responsibility. They are more socially aware and intellectually focused than younger infants and this gives them a responsiveness that can be very rewarding to the teacher. But at this level there is a growing tendency for the content of subjects to 'harden-up' and to be more precisely defined, which begins to make the construction of supportive material such as these worksheets a little more problematic. Choices can be made and it is obvious that not everyone will choose to do the same thing. However, learning, particularly within the Primary Framework is laid down in considerable detail, and elsewhere we have been able to lean heavily upon the schemes of work drawn up by the QCA.

You will find this book particularly helpful when you are limited by time or have to meet the needs of voracious learners. Supply teachers and others 'caught on the hop' will also be able to rely on this material to help them to cope with demanding days.

You will hardly need reminding that although these worksheets will support your teaching, they cannot do it for you. A whole school full of over-heated photocopiers will not make children learn; it is for you to capture their interest and to provide the intellectual stimulus and practical experience that needs to accompany learning.

Page	Activity	Objectives	Teachers' notes	NC, QCA & Primary Framework	Curriculum for Excellence (Scotland)	AT links and levels
15	Hook a word	To learn common spelling patterns for the vowel phoneme oo (as in wood).	Make sure that children recognise and sound oo before they begin.	Literacy Strand 6 – Word structure and spelling	LIT 002A/L/W – Enjoyment and choice (reading) LIT 010N/X – Tools for reading	AT2 Level 1
16	Word shop	To learn common spelling patterns for the vowel phoneme ar.	This is a variation on the previous sheet. Discuss any nonsense words which may arise.	Literacy Strand 6 – Word structure and spelling	LIT 002A/L/W – Enjoyment and choice (reading) LIT 010N/X – Tools for reading	AT2 Level 1
17	Long and short	To discriminate between words containing the long or short vowel phoneme oo.	This is a follow-up activity to the first sheet in the book.	Literacy Strand 5 – Word recognition; Strand 6 – Word structure and spelling	LIT 002A/L/W – Enjoyment and choice (reading) LIT 010N/X – Tools for reading	AT2 Level 1
18	Top-up with oil	To read words by blending onset and rhyme.	Recite examples so the rhyme 'oil' is understood. Not all combinations will make real words.	Literacy Strand 5 – Word recognition; Strand 6 – Word structure and spelling	LIT 002A/L/W – Enjoyment and choice (reading) LIT 010N/X – Tools for reading	AT2 Level 1
19	Ship ahoy!	To read words by blending onset and rhyme.	Words are generated by using the letters on the ship's wheel.	Literacy Strand 5 – Word recognition; Strand 6 – Word structure and spelling	LIT 002A/L/W – Enjoyment and choice (reading) LIT 010N/X – Tools for reading	AT2 Level 1
20	Ow!	To learn to read words containing the vowel phoneme ow (as in cow).	Read the line 'How now brown cow' aloud as a class. Children may know other similar tongue-twisters.	Literacy Strand 5 – Word recognition; Strand 6 – Word structure and spelling	LIT 002A/L/W – Enjoyment and choice (reading) LIT 010N/X – Tools for reading	AT2 Level 1
21	Make and say	To learn to read words containing the vowel phoneme ow (spelled 'ou').	Oral work must precede this activity so that 'ou' is known and recognised.	Literacy Strand 5 – Word recognition; Strand 6 – Word structure and spelling	LIT 010N/X – Tools for reading	AT2 Level 1
22	Odd word out	To identify words containing the vowel phoneme air.	Even though some sounds are the same, they can be spelled differently. Odd ones out are: 'more', 'bird', 'desk', 'torn', 'were' and 'turn'.	Literacy Strand 5 – Word recognition	LIT 010N/X – Tools for reading	AT2 Level 1
23	A necklace of rhymes	To read and identify words that rhyme.	Make sure that the children know what they are listening for as they read around the necklace.	Literacy Strand 5 – Word recognition	LIT 002A/L/W – Enjoyment and choice (reading) LIT 010N/X – Tools for reading	AT2 Level 1
24	I went to town…	To develop awareness of words that link sentences (conjunctions).	There are a number of possible answers as there are more ideas than sentence stems. Children add to each sentence stem by choosing an idea from the right-hand side.	Literacy Strand 5 – Word recognition; Strand 11 – Sentence structure and punctuation	LIT 002A – Tools for reading LIT 010N/X; LIT 121Y – Tools for writing	AT2 Level 1 AT3 Level 2
25	Joined-up thinking	To use connectives to structure a sequence of events.	Children need to decide which two phrases can be joined. The new sentences can be written in the space provided.	Literacy Strand 5 – Word recognition; Strand 11 – Sentence structure and punctuation	LIT 002A – Tools for reading LIT 121Y; LIT 125AC – Tools for writing	AT2 Level 1 AT3 Level 1/2
26	Story starts	To use the strategies of imitation and substitution to write a story opening.	Share ideas about how the 'story starts' might continue. Each opening line is a new story.	Literacy Strand 9 – Creating and shaping texts	LIT 008J/AH – Creating texts	AT3 Level 2
27	Dreamtime	To use awareness of grammar to construct sentences and use the language of time to structure events.	Discuss the pictures and clarify what is to be done.	Literacy Strand 7 – Understanding and interpreting text; Strand 11 – Sentence structure and punctuation	LIT 112N – Tools for reading LIT 003A/V – Tools for reading	AT2 Level 2
28	What happened yesterday?	To develop awareness of past tense.	The sheet should only be tackled following work on the past tense. Answers can be indicated in various ways.	Literacy Strand 11 – Sentence structure and punctuation	LIT 008J/AH – Creating texts LIT 112N – Tools for reading	AT2 Level 1

NO FUSS
PHOTOCOPIABLE

■SCHOLASTIC
www.scholastic.co.uk

Page	Activity	Objectives	Teachers' notes	NC, QCA & Primary Framework	Curriculum for Excellence (Scotland)	AT links and levels
29	Mix and make families of words	To create new words by extending root words.	Make sure the exercise is understood. Explain that the root words are 'night', 'hand' and 'day'.	Literacy Strand 6 – Word structure and spelling	LIT 010N/X – Tools for reading	AT2 Level 1
30	Shopping lists	To use commas to separate items listed within a sentence.	The commas may not be noticed so draw attention to them before you start. Note the absence of a comma before the final 'and'.	Literacy Strand 11 – Sentence structure and punctuation	LIT 121Y – Tools for writing	AT3 Level 2
31	Asking questions: What? Where? When? Who?	To turn statements into questions by adding a 'wh' word.	Build most of the questions from the words and phrases in the answers. Go through the completed example carefully with the class.	Literacy Strand 11 – Sentence structure and punctuation	LIT 122N – Tools for reading LIT 121Y – Tools for writing ENG 117T – Understanding and evaluating (reading)	AT2 Level 2 AT3 Level 2
32	Sorting syllables (1)	To discriminate syllables in words orally.	The picture cards should be cut out and mounted on card together with those from the next sheet. Children read the word on each card, tap out the syllables and sort. It doesn't matter where the dividing line between syllables is drawn for this exercise.	Literacy Strand 5 – Word recognition; Strand 6 – Word structure and spelling	LIT 010N/X – Tools for reading	AT2 Level 1/2
33	Sorting syllables (2)	To discriminate syllables in words orally.	Complete the worksheet as above.	Literacy Strand 5 – Word recognition; Strand 6 – Word structure and spelling	LIT 010N/X – Tools for reading	AT2 Level 1/2
34	At the party	To recognise question statements and use question marks.	Have a little fun talking about what is happening at the party. This could be a group or class exercise with children role playing the speakers.	Literacy Strand 11 – Sentence structure and punctuation	LIT 003A/V – Understanding, analysing and evaluating (reading) LIT 112N – Tools for reading LIT 121Y – Tools for writing	AT2 Level 2 AT3 Level 2
35	Making sense	To make new sentences through substituting words.	Children should substitute new words in the spaces to create new sentences.	Literacy Strand 11 – Sentence structure and punctuation	LIT 003A/V – Understanding, analysing and evaluating (reading) LIT 112N – Tools for reading LIT 121Y – Tools for writing	AT2 Level 1/2 AT3 Level 1/2
36	Yesterday, in the pond	To match verbs to nouns and pronouns so that writing is grammatically correct.	Valuable work comes from examining the results after the task has been completed.	Literacy Strand 11 – Sentence structure and punctuation	LIT 112N – Tools for reading LIT 121Y – Tools for writing	AT2 Level 1/2 AT3 Level 1/2
37	Mandy's muddled messages	To reorder words to construct sentences. To use full-stops and capital letters correctly.	You may wish to talk about mobile phone messages first. Direct children to look for punctuation clues and to read aloud the sentences they make.	Literacy Strand 11 – Sentence structure and punctuation	LIT 003A/V – Understanding, analysing and evaluating (reading) LIT 112N – Tools for reading LIT 121Y – Tools for writing	AT2 Level 1/2 AT3 Level 1/2
38	Wh – ch – ph	To read and spell words containing the digraphs wh, ch, and ph.	Children must be able to discriminate between the sounds produced by these digraphs in order to complete this sheet. Practise orally.	Literacy Strand 5 – Word recognition; Strand 6 – Word structure and spelling	LIT 010N/X – Tools for reading	AT2 Level 1
39	Keeping track	To extend number sequences by counting on and back on a number track.	First recite the numbers and continue the sequences forwards and backwards orally.	Maths Strand – Counting and understanding number	MNU 001B – Number processes	AT2 Level 1/2
40	Counting on or back	To find the difference between two numbers by counting on or back.	A number line or 100 square can be used as a prop if required.	Maths Strands – Counting and understanding number; Calculating	MNU 001B – Number processes MNU 002C – Addition, subtraction, multiplication and division	AT2 Level 1/2
41	Number vests	To recognise one number as 'larger than' another number.	Children will need to write down the pairs of numbers before placing them in order.	Maths Strand – Counting and understanding number	MNU 001B – Number processes	AT2 Level 1/2

Page	Activity	Objectives	Teachers' notes	NC, QCA & Primary Framework	Curriculum for Excellence (Scotland)	AT links and levels
42	Jumping in tens	To extend number sequences by counting on or back in tens starting from any given number.	Explain that the children should make the frog jump in tens for each of the questions; they should write the numbers in the boxes.	Maths Strands – Using and applying mathematics; Counting and understanding number	MNU 001B – Number processes	AT1 Level 1 AT2 Level 2
43	Odd and even numbers	To recognise odd and even numbers.	This activity is for reinforcement of the concept of odd and even numbers.	Maths Strands – Using and applying mathematics; Counting and understanding number	MNU 001B – Number processes	AT1 Level 1 AT2 Level 2
44	Number patterns	To recognise and describe number sequences.	Instruct the children to colour the squares lightly so that the numbers are not obscured.	Maths Strands – Using and applying mathematics; Counting and understanding number	MNU 001B – Number processes	AT1 Level 1 AT2 Level 2
45	Count and rule	To extend number sequences by counting on or back in steps of 2, 3 or 5.	The pictures may need a little explanation. The first sequence should also be explained.	Maths Strands – Using and applying mathematics; Counting and understanding number	MNU 001B – Number processes MNU 002C – Addition, subtraction, multiplication and division	AT1 Level 1 AT2 Level 2
46	Multiples in the air	To identify multiples of numbers.	Some understanding of the term 'multiples' is assumed.	Maths Strand – Knowing and using number facts	MNU 103C – Addition, subtraction, multiplication and division	AT2 Level 2/3
47	Words and numbers	To read and write numbers in figures and in words.	Explain the cartoon at the top of the page; the rest should follow.	Maths Strand – Counting and understanding number	MNU 001B – Number processes	AT2 Level 1/2
48	Tens and units	To learn what each digit in a two-digit number represents. To partition into tens and units.	The door numbers should be two-digit numbers only. The children could use the same number twice, for example, '44'.	Maths Strand – Counting and understanding number	MNU 102B – Number processes MNU 103C – Addition, subtraction, multiplication and division	AT2 Level 2
49	Make a date	To be able to read and write dates in the year.	There are three lists at the bottom of the sheet – one for each of the months shown.	Maths Strands – Using and applying mathematics; Measuring	MNU 001B – Number processes MNU 005L – Time	AT1 Level 1 AT2 Level 2
50	More or less	To be able to compare two numbers and to identify which number is more or less.	A prerequisite for this activity is a familiarity with the vocabulary of comparison. The last question has more than one possible answer (15, 16, 17 or 18).	Maths Strands – Using and applying mathematics; Counting and understanding number	MNU 002C; MNU 103C – Addition, subtraction, multiplication and division	AT1 Level 1 AT2 Level 2
51	Ten more or ten less	To be able to identify the number that is ten more or ten less than a given number.	This sheet should be self-explanatory.	Maths Strands – Using and applying mathematics; Counting and understanding number	MNU 002C; MNU 103C – Addition, subtraction, multiplication and division	AT1 Level 1/2 AT2 Level 2
52	Estimate and count	To begin to estimate numbers of objects.	Make it clear that estimates are not wild guesses. Some children may be tempted to count first in order to get the 'right' answer. Practise examples.	Maths Strand – Counting and understanding number	MNU 101A – Estimation and rounding	AT1 Level 1/2 AT2 Level 2
53	Rounding to ten	To round a number to the nearest ten.	Explain 'rounding' to the class. Use a number line to illustrate how to see which is the nearest ten.	Maths Strand – Counting and understanding number	MNU 101A – Estimation and rounding	AT2 Level 2
54	Halves and quarters (1)	To be able to recognise halves and quarters of shapes.	Lots of practical experience of finding halves and quarters should precede this sheet.	Maths Strand – Counting and understanding number	MNU 003H/C; MNU 104H – Fractions, decimals and percentages	AT2 Level 3
55	Halves and quarters (2)	To find one half or one quarter of a set of less than 20 objects.	Use counters or reduce the number of objects to make the activity easier.	Maths Strand – Counting and understanding number	MNU 003H/C – Fractions, decimals and percentages	AT2 Level 3
56	Fractions	To recognise one half of an object, find half of a number and know that the fraction ½ means the same as 'half'.	A little explanation may be necessary as there are quite a few words on this sheet. You could use real objects to exemplify the activity.	Maths Strand – Counting and understanding number	MNU 003H/C; MNU 104H – Fractions, decimals and percentages	AT2 Level 3
57	Halfway	To identify divisions which are halfway between two whole numbers.	Use the first example on the sheet to explain the task. Talk to the children about adding half.	Maths Strands – Counting and understanding number; Measuring	MNU 104H – Fractions, decimals and percentages	AT2 Level 2/3

YEAR 2 AGES 6-7

■SCHOLASTIC
www.scholastic.co.uk

Page	Activity	Objectives	Teachers' notes	NC, QCA & Primary Framework	Curriculum for Excellence (Scotland)	AT links and levels
58	Three hops	To add three numbers using a number line to count on.	This involves careful counting. Explain that the shapes stand for unknown numbers.	Maths Strand – Calculating	MNU 002C – Addition, subtraction, multiplication and division	AT1 Level 1/2 AT2 Level 2
59	Less than	To understand 'less than' and other vocabulary related to subtraction.	Children first need to count each set of objects accurately. Show how to find a solution by subdividing a set. Apparatus may be needed.	Maths Strands – Using and applying mathematics; Calculating	MNU 002C; MNU 103C – Addition, subtraction, multiplication and division	AT1 Level 1/2 AT2 Level 2
60	Lots of blanks	To begin to use vocabulary related to multiplication. To represent repeated addition or arrays as multiplication.	'3 lots of 2' is written as '3 × 2' in order to match the grammar of the written sentence. It can, of course, be written '2 × 3'.	Maths Strand – Calculating	MNU 002C; MNU 103C – Addition, subtraction, multiplication and division	AT1 Level 1/2 AT2 Level 2
61	Sharing equally	To understand division as 'sharing equally'.	The items can be shared out one by one. Children may want to use other strategies.	Maths Strands – Using and applying mathematics; Calculating	MNU 002C; MNU 103C – Addition, subtraction, multiplication and division	AT1 Level 1/2 AT2 Level 2
62	Halves and doubles	To know that doubling is the same as multiplying by 2 and that halving is the inverse of doubling.	Follow the doubling trail in the example at the top of the sheet. Children will need lots of practice at doubling and halving.	Maths Strand – Knowing and using number facts	MNU 002C; MNU 103C – Addition, subtraction, multiplication and division MNU 105H – Fractions, decimals and percentages	AT1 Level 1/2 AT2 Level 2/3
63	The right sign	To recognise and use correctly the +, –, × and ÷ signs.	A simple explanation should suffice. The answers can be written in the spaces or the complete number sentence can be written out.	Maths Strand – Calculating	MNU 103C – Addition, subtraction, multiplication and division	AT2 Level 3
64	Magic squares	To solve a number puzzle using reasoning.	You will need to work through the example given. This can be an activity for pairs.	Maths Strands – Using and applying mathematics; Knowing and using number facts	MNU 103C – Addition, subtraction, multiplication and division	AT1 Level 2 AT2 Level 2
65	Problems	To solve real life number problems using the operations of addition, subtraction, division or multiplication.	Children will find the problem easier to solve if they use apparatus, for example, bricks to represent apples.	Maths Strands – Using and applying mathematics; Calculating	MNU 103C – Addition, subtraction, multiplication and division	AT1 Level 2 AT2 Level 2
66	Measures	To identify appropriate units of measure.	Familiarity with measures is essential; ensure measuring equipment is accessible.	Maths Strand – Measuring	MNU 112M – Measurement	AT3 Level 2
67	Centimetre lines	To use a ruler to measure and draw lines that are whole centimetres long.	Make sure the children have decent rulers and are shown how to use them.	Maths Strand – Measuring	MNU 112M – Measurement	AT3 Level 2
68	Lines of symmetry	To recognise and draw lines of symmetry on simple shapes. To complete a symmetrical pattern.	Lines can be drawn freehand. Children will need to know what a line of symmetry looks like before attempting this sheet.	Maths Strand – Understanding shape	MTH 123V – Angle, symmetry and transformation	AT3 Level 3
69	Food on the plate (1)	To recognise basic food groups and to know that humans need food and water to stay alive.	This sheet and the next are to be used together. They work best if foods are shown and discussed. Children should link the food to the correct plate.	Science NC: Sc2 Life processes QCA: Unit 2A Health and growth	SCN 005H – Energy in food	AT1 Level 1 AT2 Level 2
70	Food on the plate (2)	To recognise basic food groups and to know that humans need food and water to stay alive.	Complete the worksheet as above.	Science NC: Sc2 Life processes QCA: Unit 2A Health and growth	SCN 005H – Energy in food	AT1 Level 1 AT2 Level 2
71	Young and old	To match parents with their offspring. To know that animals produce young, who in turn, grow into adults.	A simple matching exercise that requires little explanation.	Science NC: Sc2 Humans and other animals QCA: Unit 2A Health and growth	SCN 002B; SCN 102B – Biodiversity	AT1 Level 1/2 AT2 Level 1/2
72	Babies and toddlers	To identify differences between babies and toddlers and to know the reasons why they need to be looked after.	Talk about the issues involved. Children may want to share the experience of living within their own families, if appropriate.	Science NC: Sc1 Ideas and evidence in science; Sc2 Humans and other animals QCA: Unit 2A Health and growth	SCN 002B; SCN 102B – Biodiversity	AT1 Level 1/2 AT2 Level 1/2

Page	Activity	Objectives	Teachers' notes	NC, QCA & Primary Framework	Curriculum for Excellence (Scotland)	AT links and levels
73	Is it good for you?	To distinguish between medicines and sweets. To understand why it is sometimes necessary to take medicines.	It is worth spending time talking through the issues on the sheet. A walk around a local shop could be helpful. Stress that only doctors and adults decide when we need to take medicines.	Science NC: Sc1 Ideas and evidence in science; Sc2 Life processes QCA: Unit 2A Health and growth	SCN 009M – Keeping my body healthy	AT1 Level 1/2 AT2 Level 2
74	Exploring outdoors	To recognise that there are differences between local habitats.	Use prediction as a talking point. Help children to choose suitable sites for exploration. You could repeat the exercise under different weather conditions, such as, a dry summer's day or after rain in autumn.	Science NC: Sc1 Ideas and evidence in science, Investigative skills; Sc2 Living things in their environment QCA: Unit 2B Plant and animals in the local environment	SCN 002B – Biodiversity	AT1 Level 1/2 AT2 Level 1/2
75	A for animal, P for plant	To decide whether a living thing is an animal or a plant and to give a reason for this decision.	It is not so much the children's answers but their responses to the question How do you know? that are important. Ensure there is lots of discussion.	Science NC: Sc2 Life processes QCA: Unit 2B Plant and animals in the local environment	SCN 002B; SCN 102B – Biodiversity	AT2 Level 2
76	The same but different	To learn that humans are similar to each other in some ways but are different in others.	There are lots of possible answers here. Talk should take place before and/or after the exercise.	Science NC: Sc1 Ideas and evidence in science; Sc2 Variation and classification QCA: Unit 2C Variation	SCN 002B; SCN 102B – Biodiversity	AT1 Level 1/2 AT2 Level 1/2
77	How we are different	To understand that there are some differences between children that can be measured.	Measuring shoes is an alternative to feet. Children need to be able to measure using centimetres first.	Science NC: Sc1 Investigative skills; Sc2 Variation and classification QCA: Unit 2C Variation	SCN 002B; SCN 102B – Biodiversity SCN 009M – Keeping my body healthy	AT1 Level 1/2 AT2 Level 1/2
78	Natural materials	To identify natural materials and to appreciate that they can be changed in order to make other objects.	Wool, stone and wood – the process by which they were transformed need only be described simply.	Science NC: Sc3 Grouping materials QCA: Unit 2D Grouping and changing materials	SCN 013X – Properties and uses	AT3 Level1
79	Heat often changes things	To think about and describe the changes that take place when common materials are heated.	Note that there are a number of possible answers to some of the questions on the sheet. The clay elephant is the only non-food.	Science NC: Sc1 Investigative skills; Sc3 Materials and their properties QCA: Unit 2D Grouping and changing materials	SCN 010S – Using my senses	AT3 Level2
80	Forces	To understand that pushes and pulls are examples of forces and to recognise these forces at work.	Introduce and frequently use the term 'forces' prior to this activity.	Science NC: Sc4 Forces and motion QCA: Unit 2E Forces and movement	SCN 007L – Forces and motion	AT4 Level 1/2
81	Batteries	To learn that some devices use small batteries to supply electricity and that these can be used safely.	Explain that 'V' on a battery indicates the voltage and that the higher the voltage the greater the power. Stress the dangers of mains electricity supplies.	Science NC: Sc1 Investigative skills; Sc4 Electricity QCA: Unit 2F Using electricity	SCN 006J – Electricity	AT4 Level 2
82	Bulbs and circuits	To test simple circuits and give reasons as to why they do or do not work.	This is effectively a guide for the use of components. Make sure that the bulbs and batteries are compatible to avoid burning out the bulbs (match a 1.5v battery to a 1.5v bulb and so on). Allow plenty of time.	Science NC: Sc1 Investigative skills; Sc4 Electricity QCA: Unit 2F Using electricity	SCN 006J – Electricity	AT4 Level 2
83	Two bulbs	To make a complete circuit that will operate two bulbs successfully.	There is more than one way to make both bulbs light up: in series or in parallel. Any recognisable picture of the circuit is acceptable. at this stage.	Science NC: Sc1 Investigative skills; Sc4 Electricity QCA: Unit 2F Using electricity	SCN 006J – Electricity	AT4 Level 2
84	Who was Florence Nightingale?	To sequence events in the life of Florence Nightingale correctly.	Tell the tale of Florence's life and let the children ask questions. The sheet comes last of all. When she arrived in the Crimea 38 nurses were attending 10,000 wounded following the Battle of Inkerman.	History NC: Chronological understanding; Knowledge of people and changes in the past; Breadth of study QCA: Unit 4 Why do we remember Florence Nightingale?	SOC 002C; SOC 104E – People, past events and societies	AT Level 1/2

NO FUSS
PHOTOCOPIABLE

Page	Activity	Objectives	Teachers' notes	NC, QCA & Primary Framework	Curriculum for Excellence (Scotland)	AT links and levels
85	This is Florence Nightingale	To recognise a famous person from the past. To identify similarities and differences between what people wore then and what they wear today.	This and the following sheet are intended to support group work on Florence Nightingale. Discussion is the key.	History NC: Knowledge and understanding of people and changes in the past; Historical enquiry; Breadth of study QCA: Unit 4 Why do we remember Florence Nightingale?	SOC 002C; SOC 104E – People, past events and societies	AT Level 1/2
86	Scutari hospital	To think about what life would have been like in Scutari hospital when Florence Nightingale was alive.	This and the previous sheet are intended to support group work on Florence Nightingale. Discussion is the key.	History NC: Historical interpretation; Historical enquiry; Breadth of study QCA: Unit 4 Why do we remember Florence Nightingale?	SOC 002C; SOC 104E – People, past events and societies	AT Level 1/2
87	The Great Fire: where and when!	To locate the Great Fire in time and place.	Investigate the pictures (this can be a whole class exercise). Encourage the children to bring their personal knowledge and experience to bear on the problem. Who has been to London?	History NC: Historical interpretation; Historical enquiry; Breadth of study QCA: Unit 5 How do we know about the Great Fire of London?	SOC 102B; SOC 002C – People, past events and societies	AT Level 1/2
88	The story of the Great Fire	To sequence the events of the Great Fire correctly.	Tell the dramatic tale adding as much detail as you think the children can cope with. Have a good supply of children's reference books to hand. This sheet can be used as reinforcement.	History NC: Chronological understanding; Knowledge and understanding of events, people and changes in the past; Breadth of study QCA: Unit 5 How do we know about the Great Fire of London?	SOC 002C; SOC 104E – People, past events and societies	AT Level 2
89	An eyewitness	To understand the meaning of the term 'eyewitness'. To know that Samuel Pepys saw the Great Fire and wrote about it in his diary.	Read the extracts from Pepys' diary. Children will be unfamiliar with some of the language and so this evidence will need to be treated as a problem that needs to be solved.	History NC: Knowledge and understanding of events, people in the past; Historical interpretation; Historical enquiry; Breadth of study QCA: Unit 5 How do we know about the Great Fire...?	SOC 002C; SOC 104E – People, past events and societies	AT Level 2
90	Who's been on holiday?	To name possible holiday destinations. To collect data in a survey.	Handle the discussion sensitively – Bognor is as worthy as Benidorm. Locate the places on a globe or map.	Geography NC: Geographical enquiry skills; Knowledge and understanding of places	SOC 005G – People, place and environment	AT Level 1/2
91	Country, town and seaside	To identify places and to relate them to different types of environments.	Establish with the children the defining characteristics of 'country, town and seaside' before they begin.	Geography NC: Knowledge and understanding of places QCA: Unit 24 Passport to the world	SOC 005G – People, place and environment	AT Level 1/2
92	The beach	To identify physical features associated with a seaside holiday location.	The sheet could be enlarged to A3 size so that it can be embellished, labelled and coloured in. Children might want add people to the picture.	Geography NC: Knowledge and understanding of places QCA: Unit 4 Going to the seaside	SOC 003F; SOC105F – People, place and environment	AT Level 1/2
93	The seaside 150 years ago	To distinguish between seaside holidays past and present.	This could be linked to learning in history. Use the sheet as a focus for discussion; enlarge it if required. The picture is based on a Victorian painting of Ramsgate, by W P Frith, in 1854.	Geography NC: Geographical enquiry and skills QCA: Unit 4 Going to the seaside	SOC 002C – People, past events and societies SOC 003F – People, place and environment	AT Level 2
94	Travel brochure	To use secondary sources to find out information. To develop awareness of the wider world.	Reference books, travel brochures and the internet can make this sheet come alive. Give children time to tease out their answers. This could be done in pairs.	Geography NC: Geographical enquiry and skills; Knowledge and understanding of places.	SOC 214L – People, place and environment	AT Level 2
95	Tractor	To identify and label parts of a vehicle.	This should be fairly straightforward but note where the exhaust is. Can the children suggest why it is not in its usual place?	Design and technology NC: Knowledge and understanding of materials and components QCA: Unit 2A Vehicles	TCH 101A – Technologies	AT Level 1
96	Vehicles with a purpose	To recognise that there are many different types of vehicle made for many different purposes.	Explain what an axle is. The vehicles are: a shopping trolley, a fire engine, a multi-axle juggernaut, a caravan (one axle), a car, a military jeep, a pushchair and an ambulance.	Design and technology NC: Knowledge and understanding of materials and components QCA: Unit 2A Wheels in motion	TCH 105C – Technologies	AT Level 1

Page	Activity	Objectives	Teachers' notes	NC, QCA & Primary Framework	Curriculum for Excellence (Scotland)	AT links and levels
97	Hands up!	To identify parts of a puppet. To use a template to make a puppet.	There are two parts to this sheet – discussion and making. Show real examples of puppets or watch a puppet show.	**Design and technology** NC: Developing, planning and communicating ideas; Working with tools, equipment, materials and components; Knowledge and understanding of materials and components; Breadth of study QCA: Unit 2B Puppets	TCH 105C; TCH 107D; TCH 207D – Technologies	AT Level 1
98	Wind-up action	To learn how a winding mechanism works. To identify components in a winding mechanism.	There is no substitute for hands-on experience of winding mechanisms so provide real examples if you can. Can children think of other winding mechanisms?	**Design and technology** NC: Knowledge and understanding of materials and components. QCA: Unit 2C Winding up	TCH 105C; TCH 107D; TCH 207D – Technologies	AT Level 1
99	Hickory Dickory Dock	To design and construct a simple winding mechanism that works.	This follows on from the previous sheet. You will need to provide the materials for this activity. Give instructions for the safe use of any tools the children might employ.	**Design and technology** NC: Developing, planning and communicating ideas; Working with tools, equipment, materials and components; Knowledge and understanding of materials and components QCA: Unit 2C Winding up	TCH 105C; TCH 107D; TCH 207D – Technologies	AT Level 2
100	A fishy business	To examine and design repeated patterns. To turn a 2D design into a 3D object using paper templates and simple joining techniques.	First explore repeating pattern designs on fabrics and wallpaper. Then give two copies of the sheet to each child. After decorating with repeating patterns the fish shapes can be joined and stuffed to make a paper 3D fish. The idea can be reused to make fish using fabric.	**Design and technology** NC: Developing, planning and communicating ideas; Working with tools, equipment, materials and components; Evaluating processes and products; Breadth of study QCA: Unit 2B Puppets	TCH 105C; TCH 107D; TCH 207D – Technologies	AT Level 2
101	Bold key presses	To know that text can be entered and corrected on a computer. To develop keyboard skills through use of the backspace, space bar, shift and return keys.	Access to a computer(s) over a period of time is necessary. Introduce children to the notion of word processing. *What are the advantages and disadvantages?* Demonstrate the processes described on the sheet.	**ICT** NC: Exchanging and sharing information; Breadth of study QCA: Unit 2A Writing stories and communicating information using text	TCH 110F; TCH 111G; TCH 212G – Technologies	AT Level 1/2
102	Creating captions	To type text using and word processing program. To correct text using the backspace, space bar, shift and return keys.	Using a word processor, children write their own captions for the picture. Check that children are rereading and correcting their captions using the appropriate keys.	**ICT** NC: Developing ideas and making things happen; Exchanging and sharing information; Breadth of study QCA: Unit 2A Writing stories and communicating information using text	TCH 110F; TCH 111G; TCH 212G – Technologies	AT Level 1/2
103	A burst of colour	To known that ICT can be used to make pictures. To use the fill, paintbrush and line tools to develop a picture.	Mouse control is an element here. Demonstrate using the graphics software package that the children will use. Show examples of pictures to give them ideas.	**ICT** NC: Finding things out; Exchanging and sharing information; Breadth of study QCA: Unit 2B Creating pictures	TCH 110F; TCH 111G; TCH 212G – Technologies	AT Level 1/2
104	Turtle turns to treasure	To understand that control devices can follow instructions.	The sheet refers to a control 'turtle' but use any control device you have available. Create an island using obstacles, such as PE cones. Children record their route using shorthand (eg 'F25' for 'forward 25'). Children can then test each other's instructions.	**ICT** NC: Developing ideas and making things happen; Breadth of study QCA: Unit 2D Routes: controlling a floor turtle	TCH 110F; TCH 010J; TCH 114 – Technologies	AT Level 2
105	Which way round?	To learn the difference between landscape and portrait presentation, and to be selective in choice of viewpoint.	Make sure that the instructions are understood. There is no 'right' answer for the last task about the car race picture. It depends on what children choose to show in their picture and how it is framed.	**Art and design** NC: Exploring and developing ideas; Investigating and making art, craft and design. QCA: Unit 2A Picture this	EXA 005E; EXA 106F – Art and Design	AT Level 1
106	Design a pot	To look at the design of everyday objects. To experiment with design using first-hand observation for inspiration.	Children must look at and talk about the designs they see on everyday objects – focus on pottery if you wish.	**Art and design** NC: Exploring and developing ideas; Investigating and making art, craft and design; Knowledge and understanding; Breadth of study QCA: Unit 2C Can buildings speak?	EXA 005E; EXA 106F – Art and Design	AT Level 1

Page	Activity	Objectives	Teachers' notes	NC, QCA & Primary Framework	Curriculum for Excellence (Scotland)	AT links and levels
107	Window shapes	To learn about the similarities and differences in buildings; identifying shapes and patterns.	Use this sheet after a local walk (ideally). You could make this an 'I-spy' activity.	Art and design NC: Exploring and developing ideas; Investigating and making art, craft and design; Knowledge and understanding; Breadth of study QCA: Unit 2C Can buildings speak?	EXA 005E; EXA 107G – Art and Design	AT Level 1
108	Patterns in doors	To learn about the similarities and differences in buildings; identifying shapes and patterns.	Use this sheet in a similar way to the last.	Art and design NC: Exploring and developing ideas; Investigating and making art, craft and design; Knowledge and understanding; Breadth of study QCA: Unit 2C Can buildings speak?	EXA 005E; EXA 107G – Art and Design	AT Level 1
109	Feeling the pulse	To identify the pulse in music.	Practise clapping the quick and slow pulse of the rhyme together. Play music with a strong pulse, clapping as you go. In pairs, children can then work out a pulse for rhymes such as 'Humpty Dumpty'.	Music NC: Controlling sounds through singing and playing; Listening, and applying knowledge and understanding QCA: Unit 4 Feel the pulse	EXA 011Q – Music	AT Level 1
110	Copy claps	To identify rhythmic patterns. To combine pulse and rhythmic patterns in a performance.	Use tambours or tambourines to tap out the rhythms of names, such as, teachers' names, famous people, months of the year, local street names. Can you keep the four-beat pulse going?	Music NC: Controlling sounds through singing and playing; Creating and developing musical ideas; Listening, and applying knowledge and understanding QCA: Unit 4 Feel the pulse	EXA 011Q – Music	AT Level 1
111	A dotty game	To play and sing phrases from dot notation.	Pitched percussion instruments are ideal for use with this sheet. The tunes can be cut out and used as cards and the children can make cards for their own tunes.	Music NC: Controlling sounds through singing and playing; Creating and developing musical ideas; Listening, and applying knowledge and understanding QCA: Unit 6 What's the score?	EXA 011Q; EXA 113Q; EXA 114S – Music	AT Level 2
112	Making instruments make sound	To identify the different ways that instruments make sounds.	Access to a range of different instruments is essential. Follow up by experimenting with group performance using the instruments chosen.	Music NC: Controlling sounds through singing and playing; Creating and developing musical ideas; Listening, and applying knowledge and understanding QCA: Unit 2 Sounds interesting	EXA 011Q; EXA 113Q – Music	AT Level 1
113	Sound resources (1) Pitch and dynamics	To know that symbols can be used to change sounds. To be able to change pitch and dynamics in response to symbols.	The cards on this and 'Sound resources (2)' can be used with groups of children playing instruments to explore altering the sound their instruments make. A 'conductor' could hold up one card at a time to direct a group of children.	Music NC: Controlling sounds through singing and playing; Creating and developing musical ideas; Listening, and applying knowledge and understanding QCA: Unit 5 Taking off; Unit 7 Rain, rain go away	EXA 011Q; EXA 113Q; EXA 114S – Music	AT Level 2
114	Sound resources (2) Duration and tempo	To know that symbols can be used to change sounds. To be able to change duration and tempo in response to symbols.	The cards on this and 'Sound resources (1)' can be used with groups of children playing instruments to explore altering the sound their instruments make. A 'conductor' could hold up one card at a time to direct a group of children.	Music NC: Controlling sounds through singing and playing; Creating and developing musical ideas; Listening, and applying knowledge and understanding QCA: Unit 3 The long and short of it; Unit 7 Rain, rain go away	EXA 011Q; EXA 113Q; EXA 114S – Music	AT Level 2
115	Sound story	To learn words that describe sounds. To learn how sounds can be used to describe scenes and stories.	Read out the describing words and vary your tone to match each word. Then explore sounds/instruments that suit the description.	Music NC: Creating and developing musical ideas QCA: Unit 2 Sounds interesting	EXA 011Q; EXA 113Q; EXA 114S – Music	AT Level 2
116	The Torah: a holy book	To learn why the 'Torah' is special to the Jews and to learn how this holy book is treated.	This sheet should follow some work on Judaism. Discuss what we mean by 'holy'. Do the children have special things at home?	RE Non-statutory framework: Learning about religion; QCA: Unit 2A What is the Torah and why is it important to Jewish people?		Non-statutory AT Level 1

Page	Activity	Objectives	Teachers' notes	NC, QCA & Primary Framework	Curriculum for Excellence (Scotland)	AT links and levels
117	Rules for living	To reflect on words from the Torah that give guidance for living. To consider rules for living.	Encourage children to come up with ideas for rules. Do this as a class lesson before tackling the sheet.	RE Non-statutory framework: Learning about religion; Learning from religion; Breadth of study QCA: Unit 2A What is the Torah and why is it important to Jewish people?		Non-statutory AT1 Level 1 AT2 Level 1
118	A story told by Jesus: The prodigal son	To learn that Jesus told stories and that these stories were a way of teaching people about God and about how to behave and treat each other.	Read the story aloud and ask: *How do you think… felt at this point?* Children then complete the speech bubbles as instructed on the sheet.	RE Non-statutory framework: Learning about religion; Learning from religion; Breadth of study QCA: Unit 2B Why did Jesus tell stories?		Non-statutory AT1 Level 1
119	A story told by Jesus: Firm foundations	To learn that Jesus told stories and that these stories were a way of teaching people about God and about how to behave and treat each other.	The story can be told (or even sung) to the children. Completing the speech bubbles need not involve long sentences.	RE Non-statutory framework: Learning about religion; Learning from religion; Breadth of study QCA: Unit 2B Why did Jesus tell stories?		Non-statutory AT1 Level 1
120	Religious celebrations	To understand that religious festivals are a special type of celebration. To describe events linked to different religious festivals.	To complete this sheet the children will need more information than is provided. Use reference books or film clips to teach children about the various religious festivals.	RE Non-statutory framework: Learning about religion; Breadth of study QCA: Unit 2C Celebrations		Non-statutory AT1 Level 1 AT2 Level 1
121	Visiting places of worship	To know the importance of treating places of worship with respect. To think about how to behave when visiting a special place of religious worship.	Small mixed-ability groups are ideal for tackling this sheet. Compare the rules that each group comes up with. *Are there any rules that the groups have in common?*	RE Non-statutory framework: Learning from religion; Breadth of study QCA: Unit 2D Visiting a place of worship		Non-statutory AT1 Level 1 AT2 Level 1
122	Meet the needs	To understand that people, animals and plants all have needs.	In order to reinforce the idea that living organisms share similar essential needs, you will need to follow up this work.	PSHE and Citizenship NC guidelines: Preparing to play an active role as citizens QCA: Unit 3 Animals and us		N/A
123	Needs and wants	To understand that there is a difference between needs and wants.	Clarify the difference between 'needs' and 'wants' first, then children should follow the instructions on the sheet.	PSHE and Citizenship NC guidelines: Developing confidence and responsibility; Preparing to play an active role as citizens QCA: Unit 2 Choices		N/A
124	Saying no	To understand that they can say 'no' when something feels wrong.	Discuss the answers so that children can learn about stranger danger, cruelty to animals etc.	PSHE and Citizenship NC guidelines: Developing confidence and responsibility; Developing a healthy, safer lifestyle QCA: Unit 2 Choices		N/A
125	Red means danger	To understand that there are rules for keeping safe at home and in the street.	Colouring pencils are required. You must discuss the outcomes of this work.	PSHE and Citizenship NC guidelines: Developing a healthier, safer lifestyle		N/A
126	People who help us (1)	To reflect upon the different jobs that people carry out.	The underlying aim is to teach children respect for all people, regardless of their job, gender or race. Talk will help to draw out these points.	PSHE and Citizenship NC guidelines: Developing a healthier, safer lifestyle; Developing good relationships QCA: Unit 4 People who help us		N/A
127	People who help us (2)	To reflect upon the different jobs that people carry out.	The underlying aim is to teach children respect for all people, regardless of their job, gender or race. Talk will help to draw out these points.	PSHE and Citizenship NC guidelines: Developing a healthier, safer lifestyle; Developing good relationships QCA: Unit 4 People who help us		N/A

Hook a word

Captain Hook went to look
For a word to rhyme with **rook**

Name _____

Word shop

Shop for words with 'ar' in them.

Shopping list

c<u>ar</u>d

■ SCHOLASTIC
www.scholastic.co.uk

Long and short

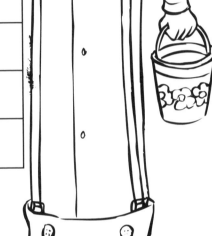

Long
moon

Short
good

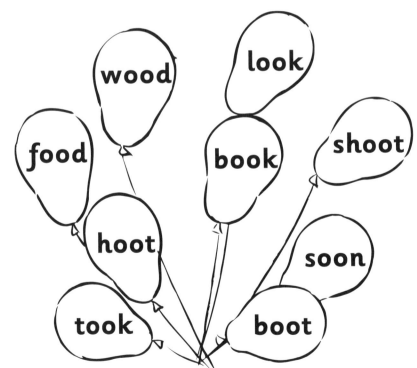

wood

look

food

book

shoot

hoot

soon

took

boot

Colour the short sound balloons.
Write the words in the correct list.

Name _____

Top-up with oil

Add oil to make words.

s   t   b   d   f   c   r   sp

_____oil

oil

■SCHOLASTIC
www.scholastic.co.uk

Name _____

Ship ahoy!

Make words with 'oy' in them.

-oy chart

Ow!

How now
brown cow?

Complete the 'ow' words

b__ __	r__ __	me__ __
c__ __	s__ __	v__ __

Make and say

Can you make and say words with 'ou' in them?

Write the words you make, and say them.

Name _____

Odd word out

Colour the odd word out in each group.

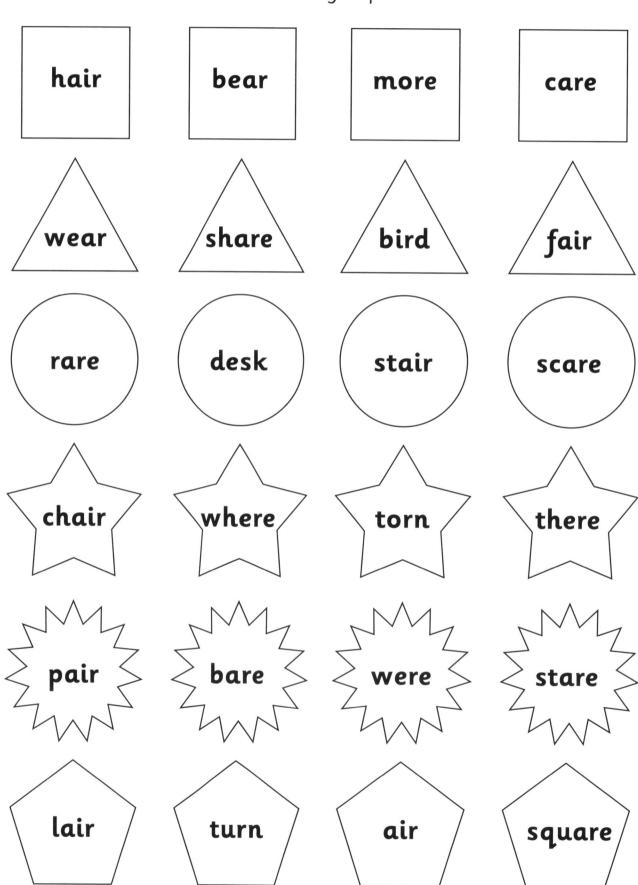

hair   bear   more   care

wear   share   bird   fair

rare   desk   stair   scare

chair   where   torn   there

pair   bare   were   stare

lair   turn   air   square

Name _____

A necklace of rhymes

Colour words that rhyme with **fear** in blue.
Colour words that rhyme with **dead** in red.

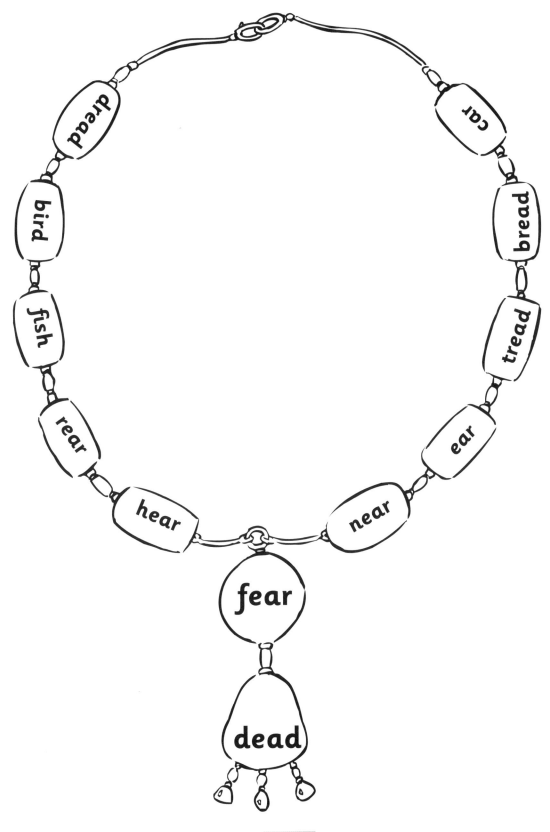

Name _____

I went to town...

I went to town and...

_____

new shoes

rain

I went to town but...

_____

money

I went to town because...

_____

birthday

o'clock

I went to town until...

_____

park

I went to town although...

_____

shopping

NO FUSS PHOTOCOPIABLE

Joined-up thinking

I ate my breakfast then...

I played football until...

I watched television before...

I went to my friend's house after...

...I went to bed.

...fell fast asleep.

...morning playtime was over.

...school had ended.

...I walked to school.

Join these sentences and write them below.

Name _____

Story starts

Finish these sentences.

Once upon a time

It started when

Suddenly

On Monday, Dan

Write a beginning of your own.

Dreamtime

Suddenly the ghost _____

_____

_____

When the dragon cried ____

_____

_____

After that I _____

_____

_____

Meanwhile, the car _____

_____

_____

rode my bike all the way home.

made loud banging noises.

jumped out of the TV.

he made a big puddle.

Name _____

What happened yesterday?

Choose the correct word to make each sentence.

Yesterday...

...Mum (went / goes) shopping.

_____

...Ali (falls / fell) off his scooter.

_____

...we all (go / went) to school.

_____

...Dad (jumps / jumped) into the pool.

_____

...I (started / start) to clean my bike.

_____

Mix and make families of words

good-

to-

night

-mare

-gown

-ly

-ie

hand

-some

-shake

-stand

-bag

-le

-writing

day

birth-

Sun-

yester-

to-

-time

-light

Name _____

Shopping lists

Commas are used to write lists.
Complete these shopping lists.

I went to market and bought _____,

_____, _____ and _____.

a hat

a pair of
shoes

a bowl

a jug

We went to the garden centre and bought _____,

_____, _____ and _____.

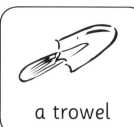

a flowerpot

a trowel

a gnome

bulbs

She went to the seaside and bought _____

_____.

a postcard

a lolly

a bucket

a windmill

Write a sentence of your own on the back of the sheet.

Asking questions: What? Where? When? Who?

Write a question to match each answer.

Answer	Question
Adam wore a red cap.	What did Adam wear?
Adam went to school.	Where _____?
Adam's birthday was on Monday.	When _____?
Auntie Jean kissed Adam.	Who _____?
Molly ate a green apple.	What _____?
Molly played at home.	Where _____?
Molly cried this morning.	When _____?
Molly loved her gran.	Who _____?

Name _____

Sorting syllables (1)

Tap out the syllables, then sort the cards into sets.

dog

kan–ga–roo

kitt–en

snake

el–e–phant

ea–gle

mouse

cow

po–ny

rat

cro–co–dile

chick–en

ra–bbit

ca–mel

NO FUSS
PHOTOCOPIABLE

Sorting syllables (2)

Tap out the syllables, then sort the cards into sets.

spi–der

ko–a–la

tor–toise

oc–to–pus

squi–rrel

li–on

swan

gi–raffe

duck

fox

scor–pi–on

don–key

star–fish

but–ter–fly

NO
FUSS
PHOTOCOPIABLE

Name _____

At the party

This party is noisy! Add the question marks, and colour in the questions.

Making sense

Fill in the gaps with **new** words. Make sense!

| Daisy | fell | off her scooter | into | a puddle. |

| Daisy | | off her scooter | into | a puddle. |

| Daisy | | off her scooter | into | . |

| Daisy | fell | | | . |

| Jake | put | his | ice cream cornet | in the oven. |

| Jake | put | his | ice cream cornet | . |

| Jake | put | | | in the oven. |

| Jake | put | | | . |

Yesterday, in the pond

Underline the correct words in the story.

Yesterday, I (see / saw) a

dog jump into the pond. A

boy threw (his / her) stick

into the pond for the dog to

(catch / caught). Three little

girls (was / were)

watching. They laughed.

One girl took (his / her)

shoes off and paddled in

the water. She (fell / fall) over and got very wet.

I (watch / watched) her mum wrap (him / her)

in a towel. She (was / were)

very cross. Then it started to

rain, so I (go / went) home.

NO FUSS
PHOTOCOPIABLE

Mandy's muddled messages

Can you un-muddle Mandy's messages?

| to the zoo. My me took dad |

_____
_____
_____

_____
_____
_____

| ice creams. two I ate |

| sick. I was |

_____
_____
_____

_____
_____

| a lion? Have you seen ever |

| I best. the parrots liked |

_____
_____
_____

Name _____

Wh – ch – ph

white	**ch**eap	al**ph**abet

Say the words. Fill the gaps.

 ____eelbarrow

 ____illip

 ____one

 ____ilippa

 ____ur____

 al____abet

 ____erries

 ____eel

 Ste____anie

 ____ip

NO FUSS PHOTOCOPIABLE

Name _____

Keeping track

Where would 32 be? Write it on the line. Where would 24 be?

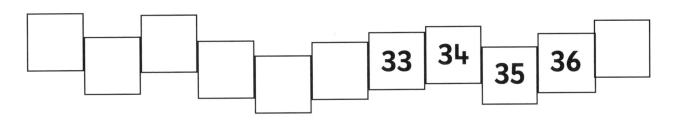

Where would 28, 31 and 37 be? Write them on the line.

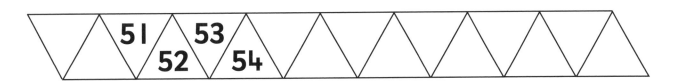

Where would 61, 57 and 49 be? Write them on the line.

Where would 82 be? What about 73 and 80?
Write them on the line.

Where would 100 be? What about 92, 90 and 99?
Write them on the line.

Name _____

Counting on or back

Count on from 22 to 27.
How many did you count?

Count on from 31 to 36.
How many did you count?

Count back from 55 to 50.
How many did you count?

Count back from 68 to 62.
How many did you count?

Count on from 81 to 87.
How many did you count?

Count back from 78 to 72.
How many did you count?

Count on from 93 to 100.
How many did you count?

Count back from 11 to 0.
How many did you count?

■SCHOLASTIC
www.scholastic.co.uk

Number vests

Make up numbers from the runners' vests on two cards. Say which is the larger number.

| 5 | 6 | is larger than | 4 | 7 |

| | | is larger than | | |

| | | is larger than | | |

| | | is larger than | | |

| | | is larger than | | |

Name _____

Jumping in tens

Write the next three numbers in these sequences.

21, 31, 41, 51, ☐ , ☐ , ☐ .

37, 47, 57, 67, ☐ , ☐ , ☐ .

26, 36, 46, 56, ☐ , ☐ , ☐ .

43, 53, 63, 73, ☐ , ☐ , ☐ .

Jump backwards

95, 85, 75, 65, ☐ , ☐ , ☐ .

88, 78, 68, 58, ☐ , ☐ , ☐ .

72, 62, 52, 42, ☐ , ☐ , ☐ .

99, 89, 79, 69, ☐ , ☐ , ☐ .

Name _____

Odd and even numbers

1 2 3 4 5 6 7 8 9 10 11 12 13 14 15

Put a ring around every other number. What do you notice?

16 17 18 19 20 21 22 23 24 25 26 27 28 29 30

Colour in the balloons that have even numbers on them.

Continue the number sequences.

21, 23, 25, 27, ☐, ☐, ☐, ☐.

18, 20, 22, 24, ☐, ☐, ☐, ☐.

What odd number comes after 5? ☐.

Name _____

Number patterns

1	2	3	4	5
6	7	8	9	10
11	12	13	14	15
16	17	18	19	20
21	22	23	24	25

Count on in twos. Start from 1. Colour each number you land on.

What sort of pattern have you made?

_____

What sort of pattern will you get on this bigger square? Count on in twos and see.

1	2	3	4	5	6
7	8	9	10	11	12
13	14	15	16	17	18
19	20	21	22	23	24
25	26	27	28	29	30
31	32	33	34	35	36

Try making your own number square that's four squares wide. What sort of pattern do you get this time?

Count and rule

Count   **Rule**

2, 4, 6, 8, 10...

Add 2 to each number to make the next one.

Complete the count and write down each rule.

3, 6, 9, 12, ☐, ☐ ...

10, 8, 6, ☐, ☐ ...

10, 15, 20, ☐, ☐ ...

Fill in the missing numbers.

17, 15, ☐, 11, 9 . . .

5, 10, 15, ☐, 25 . . .

3, ☐, 9, 12, 15 . . .

Multiples in the air

Colour the multiples of 10 in red.
Colour the multiples of 3 in green.
What do you notice about the other numbers?

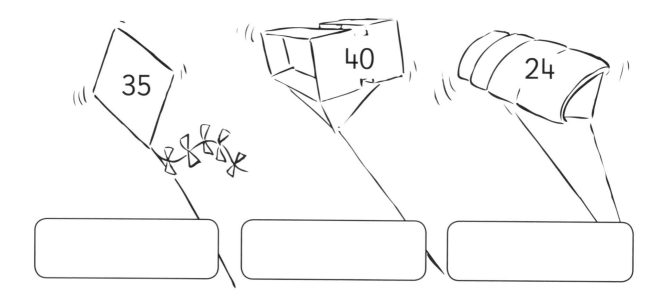

What numbers are these multiples of?

Words and numbers

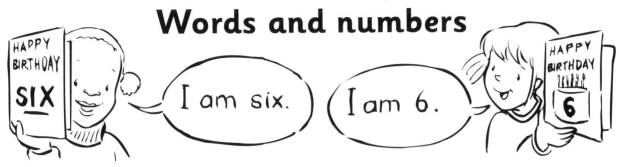

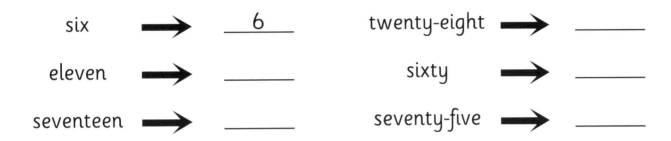

Write these words as numbers.

six   ➡   <u> 6 </u>   twenty-eight   ➡   _____

eleven   ➡   _____   sixty   ➡   _____

seventeen   ➡   _____   seventy-five   ➡   _____

Write these numbers in words.

39   ➡   <u>thirty-nine</u> _____

99   ➡   _____

32   ➡   _____

500   ➡   _____

12   ➡   _____

5   ➡   _____

Write **words** to complete these sentences.

This is PC number _____

Manchester United _____,

Leeds United _____.

Tens and units

How many door numbers can you make using these three numbers? Use two numbers each time.

Say the numbers. Fill in the blanks.

21 = 20 + 1   30 + 6 = ☐

35 = 30 + ☐   90 + 2 = ☐

57 = 50 + ☐   70 + 3 = ☐

42 = 40 + ☐   20 + 1 = ☐

66 = 60 + ☐   40 + 8 = ☐

83 = 80 + ☐   50 + 7 = ☐

Split these numbers into tens and units.

25 = ☐ + △   46 = ☐ + △

32 = ☐ + △   45 = ☐ + △

NO FUSS
PHOTOCOPIABLE

Make a date

My birthday is 29th October.

What date is your birthday? _____

What is today's date? _____

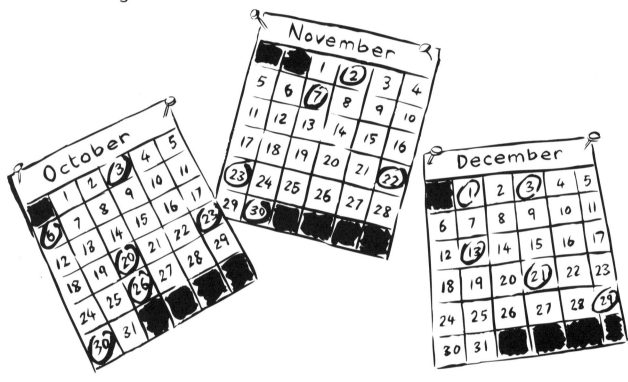

Write the dates circled on the calendar. The first one has been done for you.

3rd October _____   _____   _____

_____   _____   _____

_____   _____   _____

_____   _____   _____

_____   _____   _____

Name _____

More or less

Sunita's book
has 32 pages.

Manjot's book
has 64 pages.

Whose book has the most pages? _____

Which is more, 58p or 85p? _____

Which is more, 41kg or 74kg? _____

Which is more, 25 or 52? _____

Jo's cake

Matt's cake

Whose cake has fewer candles? _____

What number lies halfway between 15 and 25? _____

15   25

A number lies between 14 and 19. What could it be?

Ten more or ten less

What number is 10 before 67? _____

What number is 10 after 67? _____

What number is 10 less than 81? _____

What number is 10 more than 23? _____

Fill in the missing numbers on this part of a hundred square.

4	5	6	7
	15		17
		26	

Write the missing numbers in the spaces.

	ten more is			ten more is	
44	→	☐	31 ☐	→	25
53	→	☐	☐	→	41
62	→	☐	☐	→	55
87	→	☐	☐	→	99
20	→	☐	☐	→	

Name _____

Estimate and count

Estimate each number, then count and record the actual number. What is the difference between the two numbers?

How many spots?

Estimate _____

Actual number _____

Difference _____

How many bricks?

Estimate _____

Actual number _____

Difference _____

How many books?

Estimate _____

Actual number _____

Difference _____

How many birds?

Estimate _____

Actual number _____

Difference _____

SCHOLASTIC
www.scholastic.co.uk

Rounding to ten

What is the nearest 10 to 23?

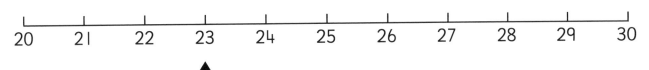

23 is closer to 20 than 30, so ⟨ 20 ⟩ is the nearest 10 to 23.

Write down the nearest 10 to these numbers?

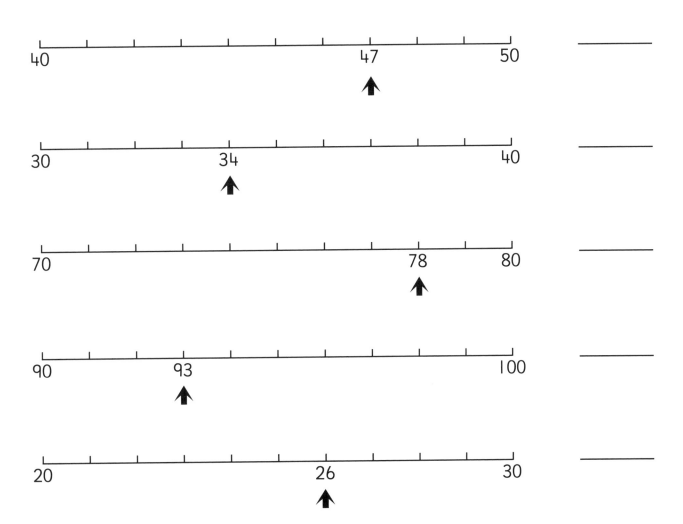

When the number is halfway between two tens, round up to the next ten.

Name _____

Halves and quarters (1)

Read and copy these sentences.

One whole = **1**   _____

One half = $\frac{1}{2}$ _____

One quarter = $\frac{1}{4}$ _____

What fraction of these shapes is shaded?

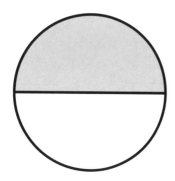 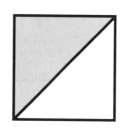 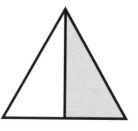

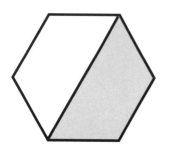  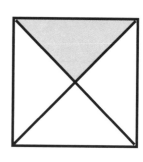

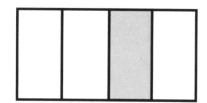  

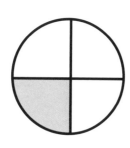 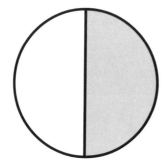 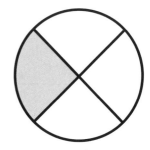

Name _____

Halves and quarters (2)

Draw a line to divide these sets of objects **in half**.

Put a coloured line around **a quarter** of these objects.

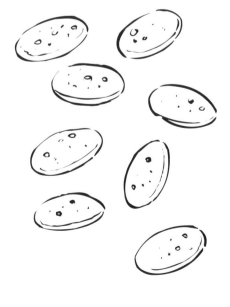

NO FUSS
PHOTOCOPIABLE

Name _____

Fractions

Copy these fractions

Colour $\frac{1}{4}$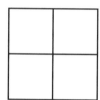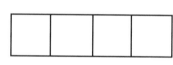

Colour $\frac{3}{4}$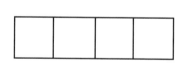

Colour $\frac{1}{2}$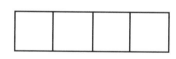

How many quarters are the same as one half? _____

How many halves are the same as one whole? _____

How many quarters are the same as one whole? _____

Halfway

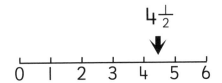

$4\frac{1}{2}$ is halfway between 4 and 5

Complete these halfway puzzles in the same way.

$2\frac{1}{2}$ is halfway between 2 and ☐

☐ is halfway between ☐ and ☐

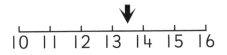

☐ is halfway between ☐ and ☐

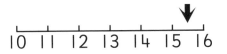

☐ is halfway between ☐ and ☐

☐ is halfway between ☐ and ☐

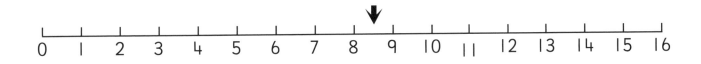

☐ is halfway between ☐ and ☐

Name _____

Three hops

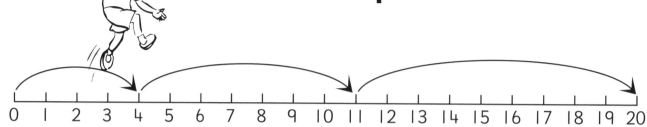

$$4 + \boxed{7} + \triangle{9} = 20$$

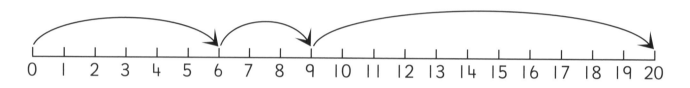

$$6 + \boxed{} + \triangle{} = 20$$

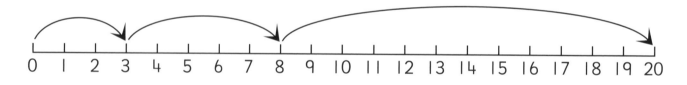

$$3 + \boxed{} + \triangle{} = 20$$

How many more sets of three hops to 20 can you make?

$$ + + = 20$$

$$ + + = 20$$

$$ + + = 20$$

$$ + + = 20$$

Less than

Fido has fewer spots than Fodo. How many fewer? _____

What is 3 less than  ? _____

What is 5p less than  ? _____

What is 8 less than  ? _____

What is 2 less than  ? _____

Fill in the boxes.

9 – 1 = ☐   8 – 2 = ☐   7 – 3 = ☐

6 – 4 = ☐   5 – 5 = ☐

3 less than 7 is ☐   1 less than 9 is ☐

Name _____

Lots of blanks

Fill in the blanks.

2 + 2 + 2 is ┌──────┐ lots of ◁ 2 ▷
             │ 3 │

2 + 2 + 2 + 2 is ┌──────┐ lots of △

5 + 5 is ┌──────┐ lots of △

5 + 5 + 5 + 5 + 5 + 5 is ┌──────┐ lots of △

10 + 10 + 10 + 10 is ┌──────┐ lots of △

10 + 10 + 10 is ┌──────┐ lots of △

 3 lots of 2 = 3 × 2 = ┌──────┐ altogether.

2 lots of 3 = 2 × 3 = ┌──────┐ altogether.

 ___ lots of ___ = _____ = ┌──────┐ altogether.

___ lots of ___ = _____ = ┌──────┐ altogether.

 ___ lots of ___ = _____ = ┌──────┐ altogether.

___ lots of ___ = _____ = ┌──────┐ altogether.

Sharing equally

Share 8 pound coins equally

between Harry and Sally.

Share 15 apples equally

between Kes, Des and Wes.

Share 8 acorns equally

between Fe, Fi, Fo and Fum.

Share 10 sweets equally

between Sunita, Prianka, Kelly, Esi and Sarabjit.

NO FUSS
PHOTOCOPIABLE

Halves and doubles

Doubling trail

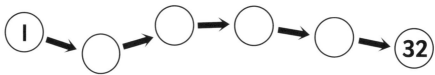

Double 2 is _4_   2 × 2 = _4_   Half of _4_ is 2

Double 3 is ___   3 × 2 = ___   Half of ___ is 3

Double 4 is ___   4 × 2 = ___   Half of ___ is 4

Double 5 is ___   5 × 2 = ___   Half of ___ is 5

Double 6 is ___   6 × 2 = ___   Half of ___ is 6

Doubling trail

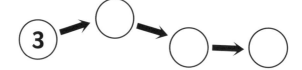

Double 10 = ___   Double 11 = ___

Double 7 = ___   Double 8 = ___

Double 12 = ___   Double 9 = ___

Halving trail

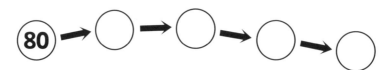

Half of 22 = ___   Half of 18 = ___

Half of 16 = ___   Half of 14 = ___

Half of 20 = ___   Half of 24 = ___

■ SCHOLASTIC
www.scholastic.co.uk

Name _____

The right sign

Write the correct sign (+, −, × or ÷) instead of ★.

7 ★ 4 = 3   ____   21 ★ 9 = 30   ____

25 ★ 7 = 32   ____   12 ★ 2 = 24   ____

10 ★ 2 = 20   ____   100 ★ 2 = 50   ____

80 ★ 2 = 40   ____   5 ★ 2 = 10   ____

64 ★ 5 = 59   ____   17 ★ 5 = 12   ____

Magic squares

1	1	1
2	2	2
3	3	3

→

1	3	2
3	2	1
2	1	3

You can rearrange these numbers so that each column, row and diagonal adds up to the **same** number. Try the same with the numbers below.

4	5	6
4	5	6
4	5	6

→

Problems

Jim and Kim share all these apples equally. Then Jim gives two of his apples to Kim.

How many does Kim have now? _____

How many does Jim have now? _____

8 people are on the bus. 6 get off. 3 get on.

How many are on the bus now? _____

 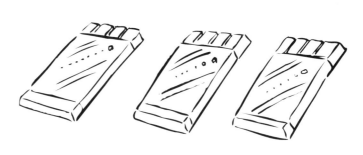

Mac bought 3 chocolate bars for 12p each.

How much change did he get from 50p? _____

Name _____

Measures

What is the best unit to measure each of these? Connect the pictures to the best unit. You can use some units more than once.

Time to boil an egg

metres

Length of a football pitch

minutes

Weight of a sack of potatoes

litres

Time to fly to Australia

kilograms

Length of a room

centimetres

Weight of sugar for a cake

grams

Amount of petrol in a car

hours

Length of an envelope

NO FUSS
PHOTOCOPIABLE

SCHOLASTIC
www.scholastic.co.uk

Name _____

Centimetre lines

Use your ruler to measure these lines. Write down the length of each line in centimetres.

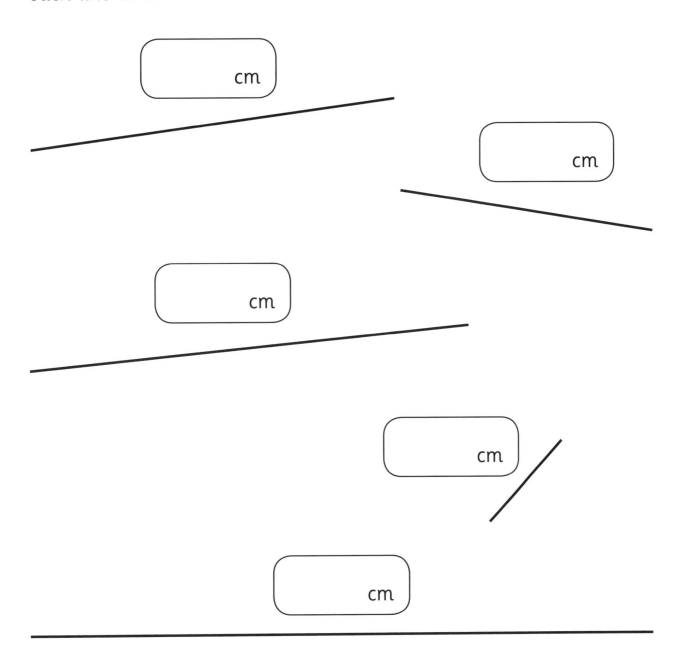

Use your ruler to draw a line that is

11cm long.

8cm long.

Name _____

Lines of symmetry

Draw a line of symmetry on each of these shapes.

Complete these symmetrical patterns by colouring.

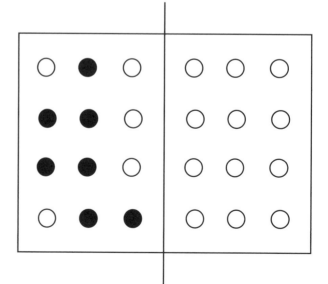

Name _____

Food on the plate (1)

cabbage

naan bread

broccoli

ciabatta

vegetables

grapes

bean sprouts

fruit

carrots

pear

bread

apples

baguette

strawberries

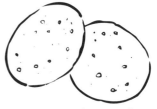
pitta bread

Name _____

Food on the plate (2)

steak

cannelloni

farfalle

spaghetti

meat

chicken

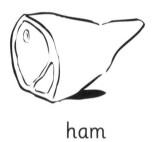
ham

made from milk

butter

Cheddar

pasta

Gouda

cream

sausages

ravioli

SCHOLASTIC
www.scholastic.co.uk

Young and old

Draw lines to match the young with their adult.

NO
FUSS
PHOTOCOPIABLE

Name _____

Babies and toddlers

How do babies and toddlers eat? How do they drink? How do they move? Cut out the pictures and sort them out.

Baby

Toddler

Talk about the differences.

NO FUSS PHOTOCOPIABLE

■**SCHOLASTIC**
www.scholastic.co.uk

Is it good for you?

Where do we get medicines from? Where do we get sweets from?

We should never eat medicines unless we are told it is safe. Circle the medicines below.

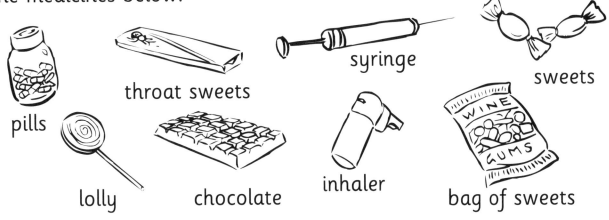

pills

throat sweets

syringe

sweets

lolly

chocolate

inhaler

bag of sweets

Why do we take medicines?	Right ✓	Wrong ✗
because we are hungry		
because a friend tells us to		
because we are sick		
because the doctor tells us to		
because we are thirsty		
because mum tells us to		
because they look tasty		
because they taste nice		

Name _____

Exploring outdoors

Choose two different places close to the school where there are different plants and animals. You could choose:

a shady area

some tall grass

a pond

a damp wall

My chosen places are:

1. _____	
Animals and plants I expect to find there.	What I found there when I looked.

2. _____	
Animals and plants I expect to find there.	What I found there when I looked.

How good were your guesses?
Explain the differences between the habitats.

SCHOLASTIC
www.scholastic.co.uk

Name _____

A for animal, P for plant

Which of these are plants? Which are animals? Write **P** next to the plants, and **A** next to the animals.

Write down one difference between plants and animals.

_____

Name _____

The same but different

These people are all different, but they are the same in some ways.

They are the same because _____

_____

_____

_____

_____

They are different because _____

_____

_____

_____

How we are different

Centimetres

25
24
23
22
21
20
19
18
17
16
15
14
13
12
11
10
9
8
7
6
5
4
3
2
1
0

Fred's foot

How many centimetres long is Fred's foot?

_____cm

How long is your foot?

_____cm

Is your foot bigger or smaller than Fred's?

_____

Measure your friends' feet. Are everybody's feet the same size?

_____

Write down some other ways in which people differ.

_____

_____

_____

_____

Name _____

Natural materials

Link each object to the material it is made from.

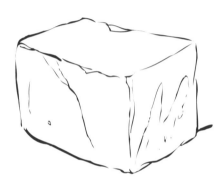

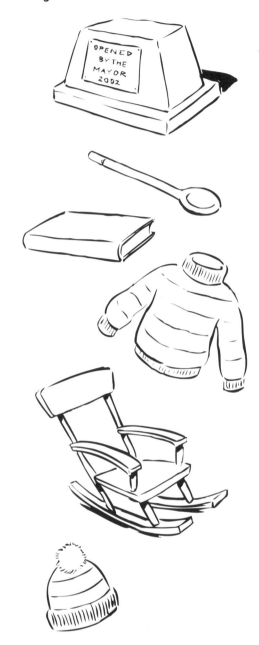

What has happened to the material?

_____

_____

_____

_____

Heat often changes things

Draw what each of these things might be like after heating. Write down why you think we might heat them.

eggs	
potatoes	
bread	
cake ingredients	
ice cubes	
clay elephant	

NO
FUSS
PHOTOCOPIABLE

Forces

pushing

pulling

Pushes and pulls are examples of **forces**.

Make a list of things moved by:

pushing	pulling

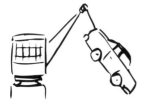    

Batteries

Batteries provide electricity. Which of these objects use batteries to make them work? Circle those that use batteries.

⚠ **WARNING:** Mains electricity can be very dangerous. It can kill!! ⚠

Here are some batteries. Which is the most powerful? How can you tell?

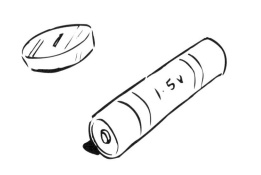

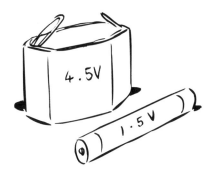

1.5V   9V   4.5V   1.5V

Name _____

Bulbs and circuits

Make these circuits.
You will need wires, batteries, bulbs, tape and a screwdriver.

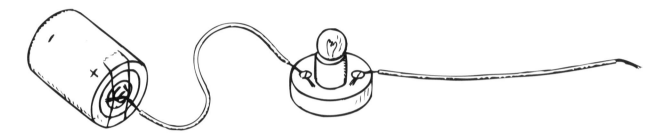

Will this bulb light? _____

Will this bulb light? _____

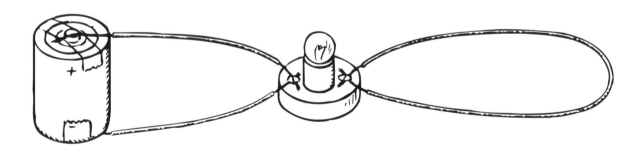

Will this bulb light? _____

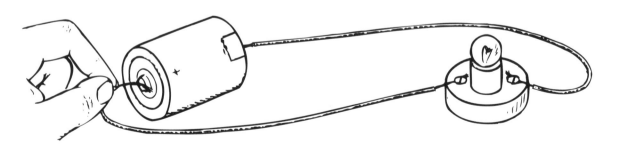

Will this bulb light? _____

Two bulbs

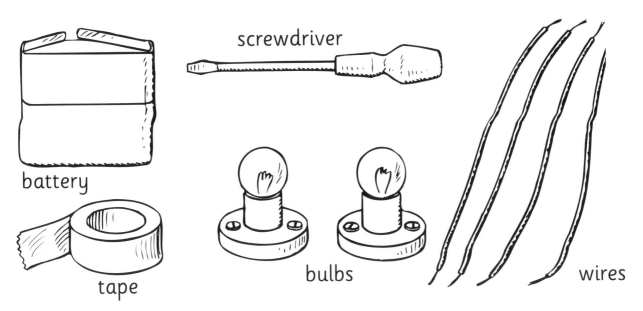

battery

screwdriver

tape

bulbs

wires

Find a way of making both bulbs light up at the same time.
Draw your circuit here.

CHAPTER 4

Who was Florence Nightingale?

Cut out these pictures of events in Florence Nightingale's life. Put them in the right order.

She trained as a nurse in Germany and France.

She saw that dirty hospitals caused death.

She was born in 1820 in Florence.

She raised money to train nurses.

During the war with Russia, she went with 38 nurses to help the wounded soldiers.

She wrote an important book called *Notes on Nursing*.

NO FUSS PHOTOCOPIABLE

■ SCHOLASTIC
www.scholastic.co.uk

This is Florence Nightingale

Look at these pictures. Which one do you think is a picture of

Florence Nightingale?

How can you tell? _____

What work might these people do? _____

Compare their clothes.

Name _____

Scutari hospital

What was it like in Scutari hospital?
Write down what you can tell from the picture.

_____

_____

_____

_____

The Great Fire: where and when?

Where is this?
How can you tell?

Which picture does each man belong to?
Draw a line connecting the person to the correct picture.

© Photodisc, Inc.

Name _____

The story of the Great Fire

Cut out these pictures and put them in the right order.

The fire spread rapidly, because it was hot and the wooden houses were dry.

The fire was controlled by blowing up houses with gunpowder so it had nothing more to burn.

The fire started in Pudding Lane.

The firefighters had only leather buckets and a few simple fire engines.

An eyewitness

How do we know what happened in the Great Fire of London?
Samuel Pepys kept a diary.

"...Jane called us up about three in the morning to tell us of a great fire they saw in the city..."

"...up at break of day to hide my things. I dig a pit to put my Parmesan cheese, my wine and other things..."

"...walking into the garden I saw how horridly the sky looks all on fire in the night. Enough to put us out of our wits..."

"...up by five o'clock, walked thence and saw all the town burned and a miserable sight of Paul's Church with all the roofs falen..."

What is an eyewitness?

Name _____

Who's been on holiday?

Ask your friends where they went for their last holiday.
Colour one square for each friend who has visited that place.

America									
Britain									
France									
Greece									
Spain									
Other place									

Which is the most popular holiday destination? _____
Can you find each of these places on a map?

Country, town and seaside

Ask your class where they stayed on a holiday.
What sort of place was it?

Which is the most popular? Why?

PHOTOCOPIABLE

Name _____

The beach

dune cliff sand waves pebbles rock pool rocks breakwater beach sea wall

◼SCHOLASTIC
www.scholastic.co.uk

Name _____

The seaside 150 years ago

Tell a story about one of the people in the picture.
How is this beach different from a beach you have been to?

(bonnet) (waves) (cliffs) (parasol) (beach)

(sand) (Punch and Judy) (paddling) (telescope)

NO FUSS
PHOTOCOPIABLE

Name _____

Travel brochure

Use books and travel brochures to match the pictures to the places.

Sydney, Australia

Blackpool, England

Florida, America

Costa del Sol, Spain

Hong Kong, China

Find each of these places on a map.

NO FUSS
PHOTOCOPIABLE

Name _____

Tractor

Draw lines to label the parts of a tractor.

engine

wheel

exhaust

tyre

axle

steering wheel

cabin

Name _____

Vehicles with a purpose

Look at each vehicle, and fill in the table for each one.

	Name of vehicle	What is it used for?	Number of axles	Number of wheels

◼ **SCHOLASTIC**
www.scholastic.co.uk

Name _____

Hands up!

How do these puppets work?

Cut out two shapes like this from material. Add eyes, ears, a nose and a mouth. Dress your puppet. What will you call it?

Name _____

Wind-up action

These toys all use a wind-up mechanism. Label the parts.

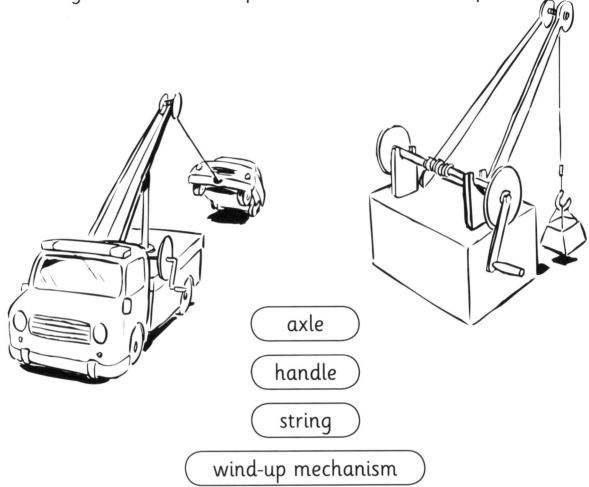

- axle
- handle
- string
- wind-up mechanism

Describe how these toys work.

NO FUSS
PHOTOCOPIABLE

■SCHOLASTIC
www.scholastic.co.uk

Hickory Dickory Dock

Make the mouse run up the clock using a wind-up mechanism.

Things you might find useful:

masking tape

cotton reels

weights

dowel rods

string

card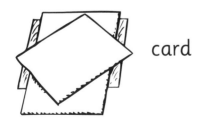

scissors

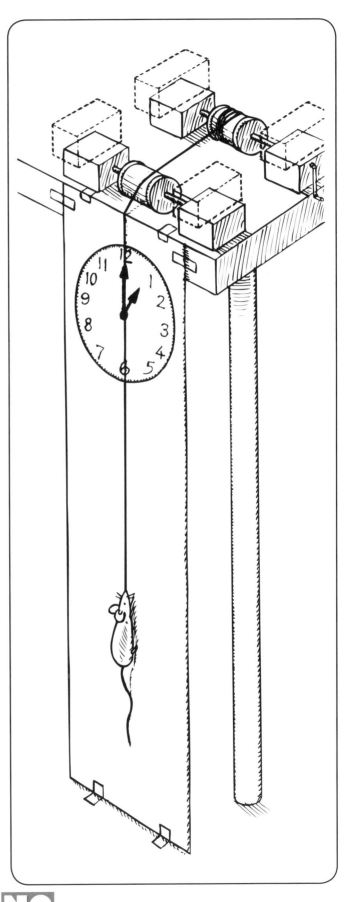

Name _____

A fishy business

Try out different patterns for your fish.

NO FUSS PHOTOCOPIABLE

SCHOLASTIC
www.scholastic.co.uk

Bold key presses

Try these:

To rub out mistakes
Use the BACKSPACE key
to rub out any mistakes.

To make a capital letter
Hold down the SHIFT key as
you press a letter key.

To put a space between words
Press the SPACE bar.

Try this:
Monday Tuesday Wednesday Thursday Friday Saturday Sunday

Can you make a vertical list?
Try making the days of
the week into a vertical
list.

Creating captions

Remember to use these keys on the keyboard:

This picture came from a story book. Which story is it?

_____

Type some more text that goes with the picture.
This is called a **caption**.

Hello Grandma. Are you feeling better?

A burst of colour

Use a drawing program to make your own brightly coloured pattern with shapes and lines like these.

Use the 'Fill' , 'Paintbrush' and 'Line'

tools to help you.

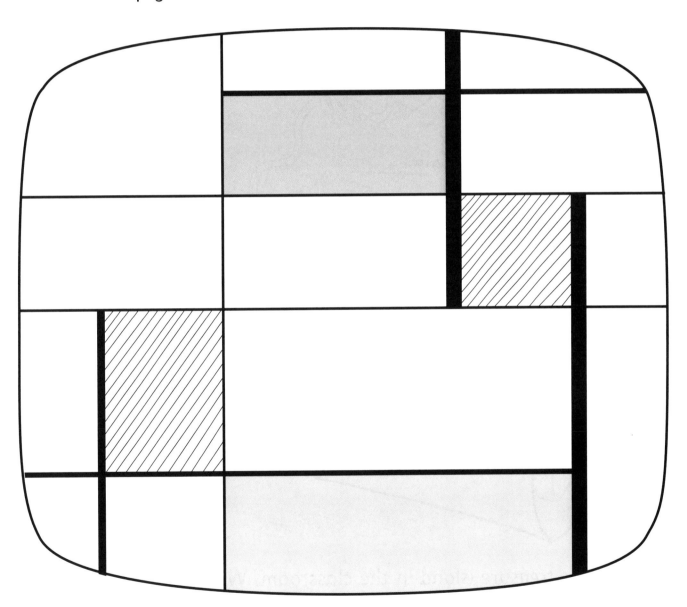

Try this:
Make a firework picture using the skills you have learned.

Name _____

Turtle turns to treasure

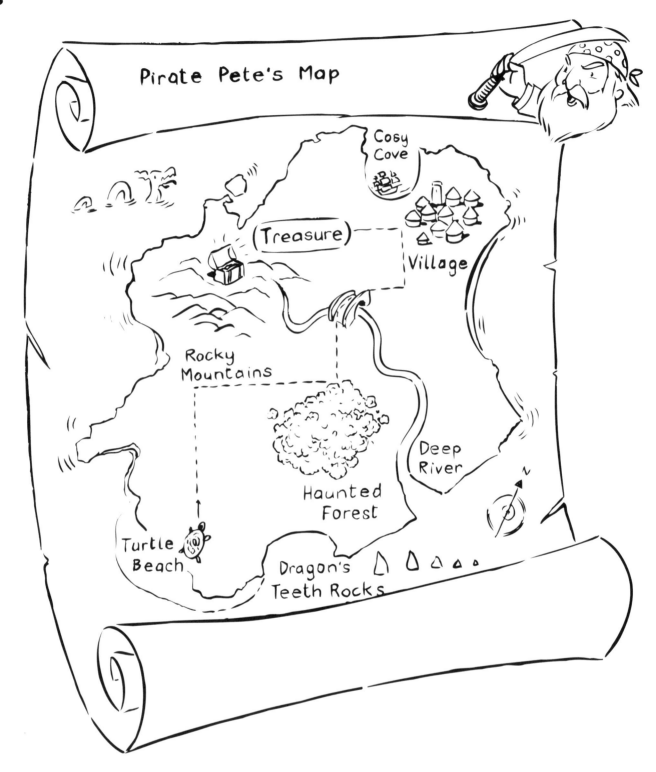

Pirate Pete's Map

Make this treasure island in the classroom. Write instructions for the turtle to use so it can reach the treasure.

F = forward   L = left   R = right

Which way round?

This is a portrait picture

This is a landscape picture

Look at these pictures. Write **P** by pictures that are portrait and **L** by pictures that are landscape.

Which frame would you choose for a picture of a car race? Draw your picture here.

Name _____

Design a pot

Write one word that each design makes you think of under each teapot.

Make your own design for this teapot.

NO FUSS
PHOTOCOPIABLE

■ SCHOLASTIC
www.scholastic.co.uk

Name _____

Window shapes

Talk about these windows. Can you see any like these?

Draw and describe a different window of your own choice.

Name _____

Patterns in doors

Talk about these doors. Can you see any like these?

  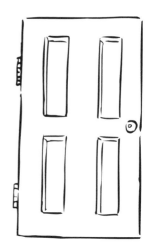

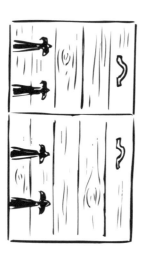 

Draw and describe a different door of your own choice.

Feeling the pulse

✖   ✖   ✖   ✖
Half a pound of tuppenny rice

✖   ✖   ✖   ✖
Half a pound of treacle

✖   ✖   ✖   ✖
That's the way the money goes

✖   ✖   ✖   ✖
POP goes the weasel!

Say the rhyme, and clap the pulse marked ✖.

●   ●
Half a pound of tuppenny rice

●   ●
Half a pound of treacle

●   ●
That's the way the money goes

●   ●
POP goes the weasel!

Say the rhyme again, clapping where the ● marks are.
Which has the quicker pulse – the first rhyme or the second rhyme?

Sing and clap the pulse to this song. Mark the words you clap on.

Here we go round the mulberry bush,

The mulberry bush, the mulberry bush.

Here we go round the mulberry bush,

On a cold and frosty morning.

Copy claps

Clap this strong pulse.

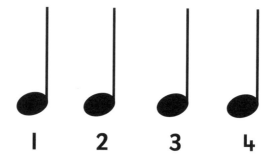

Tap the pulse on a tambourine.

Write your name here _____

Clap out its rhythm.

Clap out the name of your favourite TV programme. Can your friend guess what it is?

A dotty game

Take these three notes and two beaters. Play these tunes using the notes.

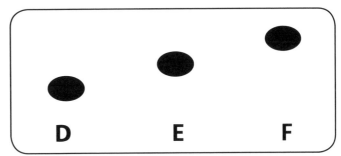

D   E   F

Sing them to **la**.

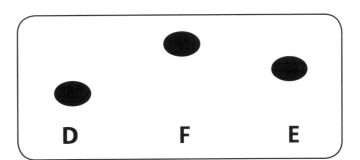

D   F   E

Can you make up your own tunes with these notes? Write it down.

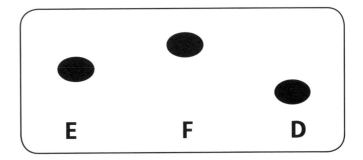

E   F   D

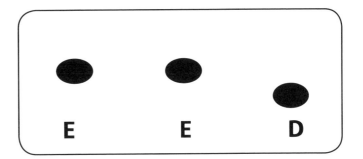

E   E   D

Name _____

Making instruments make sound

Tapping

Scraping

Shaking

Blowing

Striking

Colour the pictures in lightly.

Take one instrument to match each card.

Find out their names and write them down. Draw a picture of each instrument.

Tapping _____

Shaking _____

Scraping _____

Blowing _____

Striking _____

■**SCHOLASTIC**
www.scholastic.co.uk

Sound resources (1) Pitch and dynamics

low

high

loud

quiet

Colour the cards and cut them out so you can conduct your orchestra.

Name _____

Sound resources (2) Duration and tempo

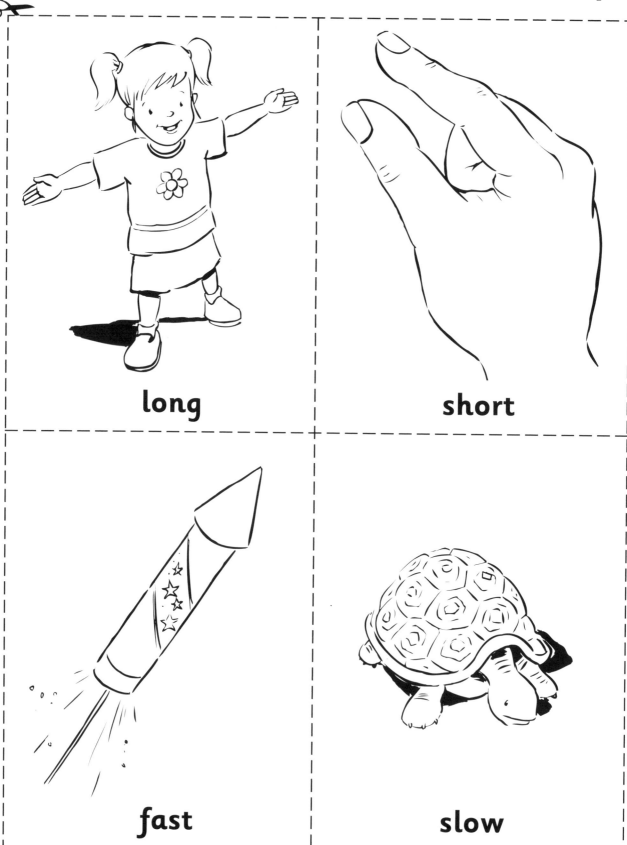

long

short

fast

slow

Colour the cards and cut them out so you can conduct your orchestra.

Sound story

What sound words might describe this picture? Make a list.

thunder	howling	_____
rumbling	_____	_____
pitter patter	_____	_____

Choose some instruments to make these sounds.

What sound words might describe this picture? Make a list.

_____	_____	_____
_____	_____	_____
_____	_____	_____

Use instruments to tell a story from the first picture to the second.

Name _____

The Torah: A holy book

The Torah is the holy book for Jews.

It was given to Moses on Mount Sinai.

It is the first five books of the Bible.

A Torah scroll is **holy** to the Jews. It is treated as very special.

The writing is not touched.

It is lifted up and shown to people.

Jews stand up and bow their heads.

Are there special things at home that you are forbidden to touch? Why?

Draw a picture of something that is special to you.
Why is it special?

NO FUSS
PHOTOCOPIABLE

Rules for living

The Jewish holy book, the Torah, contains rules for living.
This is one of the rules:

> "Show respect for old people and honour them."

How might you obey this?
Draw a picture and write a caption underneath.

_____

Make up three more good rules for living.

_____

_____

_____

Name _____

A story told by Jesus: The prodigal son

This is a story told by Jesus. Complete the speech bubbles.

A man had two sons. He gave half his land to each.

The younger son sold his land and went off to spend all his money.

He had no money and had to mind pigs. He was starving.

He was so hungry, he went home. His father was delighted to see him and made a special feast to celebrate.

When the older son came home from working in the fields, he was angry. "I work hard but you don't give me a feast."

His father told him that he was always at home, and he gave him everything. His brother had come home and they should celebrate.

NO FUSS
PHOTOCOPIABLE

SCHOLASTIC
www.scholastic.co.uk

A story told by Jesus: **Firm foundations**

The wise man...

chose a good rocky place to build a house...

the rains came down...

the house stood firm.

The foolish man...

found a sandy place that looked nice...

the flood came up...

the house fell down.

■ **RELIGIOUS EDUCATION**

Name _____

Religious celebrations

Religious festivals are a special kind of celebration. What is happening in these pictures? Write a sentence about two of these festivals.

Christmas

Christian

_____

_____

Diwali

Hindu

_____

_____

Pesach (passover)

Jewish

_____

_____

Easter

Christian

_____

_____

www.scholastic.co.uk

Visiting places of worship

Do you have rules in your home?

Take off outdoor shoes.

Keep your bedroom tidy.

Wash your hands before meals.

Dirty clothes go in the washing basket.

Finish this sentence:
In my house you must: _____

_____

_____

Churches and other places of worship are special places and must be treated with respect. Make up some rules for a school visit.

Rules

_____

_____

_____

_____

_____

_____

Name _____

Meet the needs

What is needed here? Draw or write what is needed in the spaces.

We all have needs. Write down one of your needs.

Needs and wants

Write "I want" or "I need" in the spaces.

_____
a big ice cream with chocolate.

_____
clothes to keep me warm.

_____
to meet Robbie Williams.

_____
a very fast car.

_____
to eat and drink regularly.

_____
a computer for Christmas.

Complete these sentences yourself.

I need _____
_____
_____

I want _____
_____
_____

Name _____

Saying no

Ted is not sure when to say "yes" and when to say "no". Can you help? What should he say to each of these?

Explain your answers.

SCHOLASTIC
www.scholastic.co.uk

Red means danger

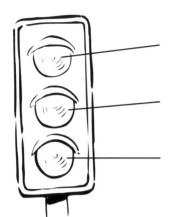

Red – danger

Yellow – take care

Green – safe

Colour the traffic lights

People who help us (1)

Who is this? _____

How does she help us? _____

_____

_____

Who is this? _____

How does he help us? _____

_____

_____

Who is this? _____

How does he help us? _____

_____

_____

Who is this? _____

How does she help us? _____

_____

_____

NO FUSS
PHOTOCOPIABLE

Name _____

People who help us (2)

Who is this? _____

How does she help us? _____

_____

_____

Who is this? _____

How does he help us? _____

_____

_____

Who is this? _____

How does he help us? _____

_____

_____

Who is this? _____

How does he help us? _____

_____

_____

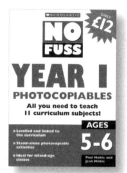

In this series:

NO FUSS YEAR 1 PHOTOCOPIABLES
All you need to teach 11 curriculum subjects!
AGES 5-6
ISBN 978-1407-10093-7

NO FUSS YEAR 2 PHOTOCOPIABLES
All you need to teach 11 curriculum subjects!
AGES 6-7
ISBN 978-1407-10094-4

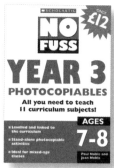

NO FUSS YEAR 3 PHOTOCOPIABLES
All you need to teach 11 curriculum subjects!
AGES 7-8
ISBN 978-1407-10095-1

NO FUSS YEAR 4 PHOTOCOPIABLES
All you need to teach 11 curriculum subjects!
AGES 8-9
ISBN 978-1407-10096-8

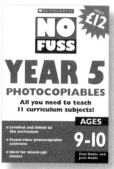

NO FUSS YEAR 5 PHOTOCOPIABLES
All you need to teach 11 curriculum subjects!
AGES 9-10
ISBN 978-1407-10097-5

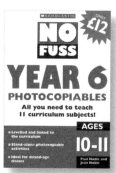

NO FUSS YEAR 6 PHOTOCOPIABLES
All you need to teach 11 curriculum subjects!
AGES 10-11
ISBN 978-1407-10098-2

NO FUSS ENGLISH PHOTOCOPIABLES
AGES 5-7
LEVELS 1-3
ISBN 978-0439-96548-4

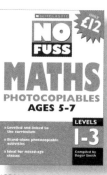

NO FUSS MATHS PHOTOCOPIABLES
AGES 5-7
LEVELS 1-3
ISBN 978-0439-96550-7

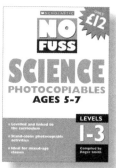

NO FUSS SCIENCE PHOTOCOPIABLES
AGES 5-7
LEVELS 1-3
ISBN 978-0439-96552-1

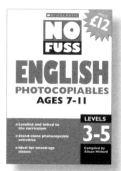

NO FUSS ENGLISH PHOTOCOPIABLES
AGES 7-11
LEVELS 3-5
ISBN 978-0439-96549-1

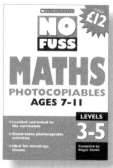

NO FUSS MATHS PHOTOCOPIABLES
AGES 7-11
LEVELS 3-5
ISBN 978-0439-96551-4

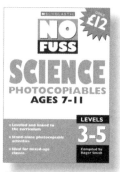

NO FUSS SCIENCE PHOTOCOPIABLES
AGES 7-11
LEVELS 3-5
ISBN 978-0439-96553-8

To find out more, call: 0845 603 9091
or visit our website www.scholastic.co.uk